Ethel Barrymore: *a portrait*

Ethel Barrymore: *a portrait*

by Mary Virginia Fox

Reilly & Lee Books
a division of the Henry Regnery Company
114 West Illinois Street, Chicago, Illinois 60610

1

The big clock in the drawing room clanged the hour of three. The sound echoed through the solemn house and announced to the family that Mrs. Drew was ready to sit down for dinner. Ethel slid off the stiff, high-backed chair and looked around anxiously for her brother John. He was forever late, getting all three of them in trouble. Ethel knew that Grandmother Drew would scold them all — even Lionel, who was never late and never once, as their mother said, "missed a cue."

The children would have liked to have had their parents here now, but both of them were on tour. Maurice, their father, was playing the romantic leading man in Sylvester Ainsworth's productions. Georgie (that was what everyone, even Ethel, called their mother) was the star comedienne of the troupe.

Ethel hurried into the empty hall, crossing the bare floors on tiptoe so that she wouldn't be scolded either for racing in an unladylike fashion or for dragging her feet to make time wait for her. Ethel found it difficult to satisfy Grandmother Drew no matter how hard she tried, and she did try.

Mrs. Drew was already seated. She was a plump woman with what the family liked to call the "Drew nose." It was long, but it in no way detracted from her aristocratic bearing. Her eyes bulged slightly, but with stage makeup no one noticed this defect. Ethel curtsied and took her place beside Lionel. Aunt Tibby was the only other member of the family in residence at the time, so John's empty chair left a larger space than usual at the long dining table. Aunt Tibby bowed her head and whispered a few inaudible words meant to be the blessing. Immediately Mrs. Drew straightened herself to ramrod posture, furrowed her brows, and uttered three words that could have been heard from the balcony of any theater: "Where is he?"

Ethel looked at Lionel, who was busily folding and unfolding his napkin in his lap. He had no answer, nor had she. Ethel wondered where little John could be. He wasn't allowed out of the house without a nursemaid. Ethel's mind slowly prepared an excuse. Before she could stammer the beginning, John came bounding into the room with a clatter of new shoes on the polished floor. Breathlessly, he crossed to his grandmother's side.

"Mum mum, have you ever seen a house painted all black?"

"No, nor have you." His grandmother cut him short. "Yesterday I gave you my last warning about tardiness. Today the punishment begins. You will retire to your room without dinner."

John started to answer, but the flash of his grandmother's eyes put a stop to his words. And her next quotation put an end to all hope of reprieve: "Stand not upon the order of your going, but go at once."

Forlornly, portraying the dramatic role of a wrongly accused defendant, John made his exit. Reaching the double doors to the hall, he glanced over his shoulder to see if someone would enter a plea in his behalf. No one spoke, and his grandmother's stare sent him scooting.

Ethel felt her tight fists relax at her side. The scene was over, but she felt sorry for John, who at this moment must be climbing the darkened stairs to the top floor of the house. Aunt Tibby attempted to make small talk about the weather and the state of the roses in the garden. Ethel knew that her aunt long ago had learned to erase all unpleasantness from her mind by ignoring it. But Mrs. Drew did not answer, which was a warning to Ethel not to expect favors. Mummum's disposition was apt to swing from strictest discipline to the most lavish indulgence, and only by carefully reading her mood of the day could Ethel and Lionel know how to space their own requests.

It was a lovely, warm day, and Ethel had hoped that if Aunt Tibby could be spared for just one hour, Ethel could go to the park and see the trained dog act scheduled for the afternoon. She wouldn't dare ask now. Ethel tried to think of something she could do by herself, such as dressing up in some of Georgie's costumes, but Grandmother might object even to that if she picked the wrong finery. Ethel waited to be dismissed.

When Mrs. Drew finished her last sip of mint tea, she turned to the two young Barrymores and said, "If you can stay out of trouble, I'll let Kitty take you to Mrs. Garrett's."

Ethel looked up from her plate in surprise. This was almost as good as the dog show. Kitty was their nurse; Mrs. Garrett was the seamstress who took charge of all Grandmother's costumes when she was playing at the theater. Mrs. Garrett lived in a small frame house in the middle of Philadelphia, but it had a yard spilling over with flowers and kittens. Her kitchen had beautiful smells and was not off limits to children, as was the smoky oven-and-sink room of the Drew residence.

Ethel bounced off her chair and hurried to the door. A command from her grandmother stopped her before she had reached the exit. "You will proceed 'wisely and slow.'" Ethel slowed her steps immediately.

"Be gone with you," Grandmother said. She sounded just like the Red Queen in *Alice in Wonderland* saying, "Off with her head!" Ethel didn't notice that the faint glimmer of Mum mum's smile hinted that her tone of voice belied the meaning.

Lionel was directly behind Ethel, and the two, now that they were out of sight of the fearsome Mrs. Drew, ran to the front door, where Kitty had been waiting all along. The carriage was not in sight, but Ethel didn't mind. Walking gave her more opportunity to gaze at the sights along the way to Mrs. Garrett's. The stonecutter across the street was chipping away at a stolid angel that would later come to rest in some quiet cemetery. In deference to this morbid art work, Georgie had named their house "The Tomb of the Capulets." Ethel had already decided she would become a sculptress herself someday.

The little shop where Mum mum often bought yards of gay colored ribbon was right next to the tobacconist, and after that was the print shop where Mr. Larsen turned out all the playbills and programs for Grandmother's Arch Street Theater. Lionel wanted to stop and watch the clanky press operated by the young man in the leather apron.

"Oh, come on, Lionel," Ethel said with exasperation.

" 'Little Miss Boss-Skirts' again. If it was something *you* wanted to see, there'd be plenty of time. Who wants to play with kittens? They make me sneeze," teased Lionel.

"Do cookies make you sneeze, too?" Ethel retorted.

Lionel's frown disappeared. He started off down the street at such a fast pace that Ethel had to run every few steps to catch up. Kitty was left far behind.

"Lionel, wait a minute," Ethel called.

Lionel broke his stride only briefly. "So now you're 'Miss Can't-Make-Up-Your-Mind.' "

"Oh, be quiet."

"I won't," said her brother.

"Well, I will then," Ethel declared.

"Bet you can't be quiet and not say a word from this minute until we get to the house," said Lionel.

"Oh, yes, I can."

Lionel howled with laughter. "See, you lost already."

Ethel stamped her foot angrily and bit her lip so she wouldn't say more. She raised her head regally and marched ahead. When they came to the flowered fence, Lionel climbed over the gate, leaving Ethel to struggle with the rusty latch. Almost immediately, Mrs. Garrett appeared on the front porch. She was a buxom woman who hardly seemed to have reached grown-up height herself.

"Bless my soul, you're right on schedule. Kitty told me to be expecting you, if Mrs. Drew didn't change her mind, that is." Then she looked around her and frowned. "Where is little John?"

"He was late for dinner," Ethel explained.

"And he such a wee one," Mrs. Garrett sighed in sympathetic concern. "We'll see what we can find to wrap up and send home to him."

By this time Kitty had breathlessly joined them. "I don't know whether Mrs. Drew would approve, seeing as how . . ." she started to say.

"Am I supposing she gave particular orders that I not send a gift for his birthday, for instance?" Mrs. Garrett asked.

"That's a month off," Kitty protested.

"Is that right? I can never keep dates straight, which is as good an excuse as any, if you should need one, that is."

As the head conspirator, Mrs. Garrett led them a few short steps to the kitchen. There on the table was a platter full of warm, puffy oatmeal cookies, sticky and bulging with raisins and dates.

"I expect you'd best be sampling these to see if they're good enough for that birthday gift," she chuckled. "I'll do the talking while you fill your mouths."

Neither Ethel nor Lionel really heard any words while they concentrated on the delicious treat. Ethel had never tasted anything so good. Mary Aggie, the cook at the Drew house, managed unusual meals at unusual hours, but because Mrs. Drew felt that "a trim mind and a trim figure don't go with a pound of sugar," sweets were barred from the daily menu.

Only when Ethel heard, "One's a tiger and two are coal black," did she stop reaching for her third cookie.

"Has Mahitabel had kittens already?" she asked.

"A week ago," Mrs. Garrett said.

Ethel headed for the door, but Lionel stayed next to the cookie platter.

"Joshua Templeton brought his nanny goat over for me to tend until he gets back from seeing his sister in the country," Mrs. Garrett announced casually.

"Could I ride her?" Lionel asked with enthusiasm.

"Now that's a silly question and one she'd be answering herself," Mrs. Garrett said. "You wouldn't be on her back a minute, and don't you try it."

The screen door banged for the second time as Lionel bolted out the door, one cookie in his hand and one in his pocket. A line of fresh, clean linen from the Drew household festooned one side of the small yard, and behind the clothesline Lionel found the black and white nanny goat munching on what was left of a ring of grass already cut short by her appetite. The nanny was tied to a stake that kept her from sampling the sweet peas draped over the broken fence. A tub of bluing water left over from the batch of laundry was balanced on a plank between two sawhorses. Lionel timidly reached over to pat the nanny's ridged nose. She tossed her head and backed up a few steps.

"We just got to get used to each other, that's all." Lionel spoke softly to the goat, who now caught sight of the cookie. In a flash she snatched it from his hand, swallowed it, and nuzzled around for more.

"There now, see, we're friends," said Lionel with more confidence than he felt.

Ethel had already found the kittens tumbling around their mother on the grass. She laughed as they sprawled over one another trying to bat a tail or chew an ear. She picked up one of the black kittens. It mewed to be put back in the jungle of grass.

"Come watch," Ethel called to Lionel, but her brother was busy untying the goat's tether so that the nanny could sample a fresher plot of grass instead of the cookie in his pocket. Suddenly the goat pulled loose from Lionel's grasp and bounded across the yard past the clothesline.

Ethel looked up just in time to see the plank and sawhorses and tub of water clatter to the ground beside her. The water covered her with a whoosh, soaking her with a light blue stain. It was a full moment before she realized what a horrible thing had happened. She was wearing her newest gingham dress with the wide, ruffled collar. Not only was her dress soaked, but her long, straight hair was now hanging in dripping strands down her back.

Lionel was shouting, "Come back! Come back!"

Kitty and Mrs. Garrett rushed to the back door stoop. "Saints beware!" Mrs. Garrett exclaimed. Kitty let out a shriek of despair. She rushed toward the dripping Ethel, while Mrs. Garrett put her short legs into motion as fast as she could to catch the nanny before the goat could escape to the street. It was Lionel who at last caught the dangling rope, just as the goat was cutting through the hedge of sweet peas.

Both Kitty and Ethel were in tears. "It wasn't my fault," sobbed Ethel.

"What am I to do?" wailed Kitty.

"Let's mop that dress before the bluing sets," was Mrs. Garrett's practical suggestion. More water was splashed on the gingham, and Ethel shivered.

"I can't go home this way," she said.

"Now, it won't be so bad," said Mrs. Garrett. "You'll dry off in no time. And if your grandmother has a few harsh feelings about it, you can tell her it was my fault for having left the tub where I should have known . . ."

Ethel turned to her brother. "No, it was your fault, Lionel," she cried. "You let the goat loose. Oh, I hate you. I hate you."

Lionel headed for the front gate and said, "I'm going home."

The thought of returning home once more turned Ethel's tears to sobs. "If we get home now, your grandma may be taking her nap," said Kitty hopefully.

Ethel thought briefly of running away from everybody and never going back to Twelfth Street, but Kitty grabbed her by the hand and pulled her out through the front gate. Ethel squinted so that her eyes were nearly closed. It helped her to pretend that no one could see her, either. When they were almost home, a young boy on a bicycle shattered the illusion.

"Whatcha do, fall in a rain barrel?" he called out.

Ethel's shame abruptly turned to anger. She raised her head, straightened her shoulders, and paraded like a queen down the street in her dripping gingham. Later in life, Ethel was to remark that this was her most superb piece of acting.

Kitty knocked timidly at the back door. Mary Aggie, the cook, was nowhere about. They retraced their steps to the front door and waited for Lily, the maid, to answer the bell. Mrs. Drew was just crossing the hall from the drawing room to the library when the door opened.

Her eyes opened wide. Her face reddened. Her voice trembled as she whispered, "This is entirely too much."

"But it was Lionel . . ." Ethel began.

Mrs. Drew's hand went to her head as if to stroke an aching temple. Her voice gained volume in a rolling wave. "I don't care where Georgie and Maurice are engaged at the moment," she said. "I will send word for them to come and get you two at once. It is high time they realized what kind of children they are raising."

Ethel was trembling, but the punishment seemed the very answer to her prayers.

2

Grandmother Drew could never have guessed what a delightful punishment she had planned. Georgie and Maurice were ordered home, but they were far from being furious at the interruption of their plans, for it happened that the summer run of Shakespearean plays had been disappointing. The company was being brought back earlier than originally scheduled.

Georgie breezed into the great hall with her assortment of luggage — trunks and hatboxes and wig boxes and a makeup box that folded out into a miniature dressing table. She was like a spring shower that freshens the atmosphere. Tall, fair, and slender, she was wearing a sea-blue rustling taffeta gown that swept the floor in a tiny train. Her sea-blue eyes darted from one person to another as if she were afraid she might miss some fun. Georgie swept up each of her children briefly in an embrace. A scent of violets hovered about her. Ethel could never think of her mother without breathing deeply and remembering the lovely fragrance of the perfume Georgie always wore.

Maurice appeared in a top hat, as he always did from mid-morning on (and he rarely was seen before that hour). A boutonniere decorated his lapel. He was startlingly handsome, with a classic profile and a rugged cleft in his chin. His regal bearing and stage presence never relaxed, no matter how intimate the audience.

Ethel still couldn't understand why Maurice should wear that funny eyeglass in just one eye. Whenever the girl dared ask her mother about it, Georgie explained logically that it was quite the fashion for men to wear a monocle in England, and since that was where Maurice had been born, it would be unseemly for him not to follow the mode of the hour.

Even Mum mum seemed to relax her sternness when Georgie and Maurice Barrymore arrived. Surprisingly, the subject of the bluing catastrophe was never mentioned. Mrs. Drew's explanation as to why she could no longer be responsible for the children was that she was about to go on tour in the role of Mrs. Malaprop. Georgie and Maurice, it seemed, were equally involved with plans.

"Madame Modjeska has asked that I play Romeo opposite her Juliet in a new production," Maurice announced.

Mrs. Drew seemed not at all impressed. "You will be working with a witch, Maurice. She is a master of upstaging. She overdoes her passion, whether on stage or off. Watch that she doesn't twirl her pearls during her death scene."

Maurice was not one to take advice from another actor, even one as imposing as his mother-in-law. "She will do well to keep the audience on her side even for one scene," he said.

Georgie broke in. "You're both right," she said with a smile. "She's a witch, and you're a genius, my dear." She lightly patted her husband's arm and then turned to her three children, standing silently and attentively nearby. "And just think, we will be traveling by private car on the train. Madame Modjeska has said that I can bring you children with me." Again Georgie swept Lionel and Ethel into her arms.

"We'll be going on tour? All over the country?" Ethel asked. "Will we eat on the train, sleep on the train? How do you take a bath on the train?" Her questions tumbled out, one after the other.

Georgie laughed. "Isn't it more fun to have surprises? You'll find out in good time."

"And time is of the essence," interrupted Maurice. "Tidy up your things and have them ready for packing. We leave tomorrow."

"All except little John, of course," said Georgie. "He'll stay here with Kitty."

Ethel was upset. No matter how much trouble John caused, it didn't seem fair that he should be left behind. A month later she had changed her mind, for while John was having a great time at home without any family around, Ethel was bored to distraction. The private car was a lavish house on wheels, but a rather crowded one. Madame Modjeska had brought along her Polish maid and her French chef. With luggage stored between the parlor section and the sleeping compartments, there was nowhere to play and, of course, no one to play with.

Lionel was no help at all. He spent most of his days flat on his stomach drawing pictures of horses and barns and a nearly perfect portrait of Madame Modjeska. No one dared show it to the lady herself because her regal nose had been lengthened a shade longer than necessary and her pompadour frizzed a bit higher than current fashion. Yet the likeness was uncanny.

Supper was always served early, after which Modjeska would retire to her boudoir, as she called it, to apply her makeup. The traveling schedule had been carefully planned by her husband, Count Bozonta, the manager of the troupe, who was always one stop ahead of them. At some time during each day, the train would shudder to a stop. The private car would be nudged gently onto a siding off the main track, where the count would be waiting in a carriage to meet his wife and her party. If the performance was for one night, which was usually the case, their sleeping quarters remained aboard the train. Late in the night, Ethel would wake to hear a clanging and switching as the car again got under way.

The children were permitted to attend the theater only once, and this was arranged by Modjeska over Georgie's protests.

"It is time they learned their craft," Madame said.

"I have no intention of letting my children ruin their lives on the stage," Georgie answered.

"Ruin their lives? What a foolish statement, when this may be their only escape from life's boredom," Madame declared.

Georgie did not win the argument, so one evening Ethel thrilled to the sight of stage lights and the sound of applause. She and Lionel were allowed to watch from the wings while actors and actresses slipped from the world of reality into make-believe. This was Modjeska's world. Her voice, without straining, could send a whisper to the farthest balcony, while every movement of her body was planned to catch the mood of a character. Modjeska was not a beautiful woman when seen on the near side of the footlights, but her personal magnetism on stage captured her audience.

How proud Ethel was of Maurice, too. There was a surge of applause when he made his first entrance. He looked so handsome, so strange, in his shoulder-length wig. Georgie was playing only a minor role, but her costume was purple, embroidered with huge paste pearls that looked very real. Ethel struggled to follow the lines. She couldn't understand many of the words, but by the time Juliet had collapsed on stage, Ethel's cheeks were wet with tears.

There were five curtain calls that evening, and a huge bouquet of flowers was presented to Modjeska by an admirer. Ethel wished she had something to give to Madame herself to say "thank you" for such a wonderful evening.

Before the last stage light was turned down, the cast had scurried to their dressing rooms to remove the grand costumes and wipe off the glow on their cheeks. Only the two stars, Modjeska and Maurice, had dressing rooms of their own. The rest of the cast made do with whatever space could be curtained off from the huge backstage blackness. Ethel timidly knocked on Maurice's door. He answered it gruffly, then smiled when she entered. He asked, "And how did you like it, little one?"

"You were wonderful, Maurice, wonderful. I cried in the end when you died."

"Good, that is what I meant to have you do. There wasn't a dry eye in the audience, not one, did you see? I was at my best tonight. Now run along and see your mother."

Turning to go, Ethel noticed a bouquet of lilies that had just been delivered to the dressing room.

"May I have one, Maurice?" she asked.

"Why, yes, take what you want."

Ethel picked two white blooms from the bouquet and hurried to Madame Modjeska's dressing room. She hadn't thought what she would say to the great actress, but the flowers would help her think of something. When the door opened, Modjeska took one look at Ethel and her present and slammed the door. Ethel stood in the darkened hallway, dismayed. What had she done? From inside the dressing room she could hear shouts and a torrent of foreign words.

Soon Maurice was sent for. Ethel edged farther back in the darkness. No one bothered to close the door.

"You have tricked me. You sent the child on purpose to upset me, to spoil the rest of my performances," Madame shouted.

"Stop yelling like a banshee," Maurice shouted back. "Who hās tricked you? What about the child?"

"You know perfectly well. She came here with lilies, your daughter. Where else could she have gotten them?"

"And what's wrong with lilies?" Maurice asked, out of patience with Modjeska.

"So you admit it. You know they are bad luck. I won't have them in the theater."

Maurice threw back his head and hooted with laughter. "Lilies, beautiful lilies. Why, they brought me luck tonight. I was magnificent."

"You're a monster." Modjeska picked up a powder pot to throw. Maurice ducked, and the pot clattered against the door as he slammed it behind him.

Only then did he see Ethel in the shadows. "Come along, daughter," he chuckled. "From now on I'll send lilies for every performance."

Maurice never did send the flowers, and to keep peace in the company, he even went so far as to make an apology of sorts, but it took Modjeska several hours of prayer and several days of devout candle-burning before the little shrine set up in the lounge car to "break the spell," as she explained it.

The little statue and the candles had always been a mystery to Ethel. When she finally asked Georgie why the candles were lit even in daylight, Modjeska overheard her question.

"Doesn't she know anything about the Catholic church?" Madame asked angrily.

Georgie replied, a bit untruthfully, "She says her prayers every night."

"Has she been baptized?"

Georgie shook her head.

"That is shocking," declared Madame.

Georgie looked frightened, but Maurice was only amused. "She has been taught the Commandments, my dear, which I believe is equally important," he said.

Modjeska ignored the personal message and continued, "We will see that the children are baptized in the true church, but first, as parents, you must read the catechism yourselves."

"That, Madame, is no concern of yours. If I prefer to kneel before a heathen idol, I will do just that," Maurice answered.

"You must not say that, Maurice, even in jest." Georgie was visibly frightened.

"I will leave the religion to the two of you," Maurice said as he turned to go.

Modjeska knew better than to attempt Maurice's conversion, and so instead she concentrated on the more susceptible Georgie Barrymore. She presented Georgie with her own Bible, missal, and catechism. To everyone's surprise, Georgie spent hours reading them. Before the end of the tour, Georgie announced that indeed she was ready to join the Catholic church. Madame Modjeska embraced her and at once declared that Georgie was her very closest friend in the world.

"We'll have the baptism for the children in New York," Madame said. "I have friends there, and it will be easier to find proper godparents. The count and I will, of course, stand

up for Lionel. Now, for Ethel, I thought we'd ask Veronica
Murray. I have known her for years. She runs a fashionable
boardinghouse for actors. We'll let her find another good
Catholic."

On the chosen day, Miss Murray turned up with a stranger
named Perugini. Both Ethel and Georgie were dressed in
white, Lionel in shiny blue serge. Madame and her count
were impressively attired in solemn black. Maurice was persuaded to come to the service, but he sat in the very back
pew of the chapel.

Later, Ethel could remember only a dimly lit church, the
smell of smoky candles, a priest in long black robes, and the
muttering of a few strange words. The stage performance of
Romeo and Juliet had been more impressive, yet in later
years the baptismal service was to mean a great deal to Ethel.

Finally the tour was coming to an end, and Ethel was glad.
The little girls waving at the crossings seemed to be having
such fun. The sleeping berth, Ethel's only private spot in the
whole world, seemed to be getting smaller and smaller. She
wished the clickety-clack of the moving train would be silent
for just one night.

Again it was Maurice who made an announcement that
was to change their lives. He chose Monday noon, when the
family was gathered around the dining table.

"It is with regret, Madame," he said, bowing low to
Modjeska, "that at the end of this tour our paths must
separate."

Georgie looked up in surprise. Modjeska's frown was
caused less by disappointment than by her impatience with
Maurice's continual speech-making, off stage as well as on.

"Yes, we will be returning to London. We will . . ."

"But, Maurice, how are we going to pay the passage?"

Georgie interrupted. "We have barely put aside enough savings to pay our costume bills, and with the children along . . ."

"I have just heard that I have been named beneficiary in the will of a departed aunt," replied Maurice. "The counselor at law has forwarded a substantial sum so that we may proceed without delay to England, where I will be able to make arrangements for the investment of the rest of my inheritance."

Georgie jumped to her feet. "Oh, Maurice, why didn't you tell me?" She hugged Maurice and danced him around in a circle until the swaying car sent them tumbling onto a sofa, Georgie in a spasm of laughter, Maurice's dignity strained beyond repair. Madame left immediately for her boudoir.

3

London was a magical place. Maurice's inheritance had provided them with a luxurious, though drafty, house near Lords' Cricket Ground. In 1884 it was the custom for fashionable ladies and gentlemen to gather at the cricket ground — as much to inspect each other as to watch the cricket matches. The nearby house was full of Maurice's old friends, whom Georgie at once captivated. She loved to entertain, and now that she could do so properly, the drawing room was never empty.

At first Georgie insisted that Ethel join the family and their company at tea. These were the only hours that Ethel dreaded. If she had been beautiful like Georgie, guests could have praised her curls, her eyes, and her dainty chin; but she wasn't pretty in that way. Ethel's hair was pale and straight, her nose a little too long. She felt that her eyes bulged like Grandmother Drew's. And she could never be clever in front of guests, reciting poetry, as Lionel was sometimes forced to do against his will. When Ethel was brought forth for company inspection, she was terrified and spent most of her time looking at the toes of her shoes.

Only after a particularly disastrous afternoon did Georgie finally give up on her daughter's social training. When Ethel entered the drawing room that day, one guest was already seated, surprisingly enough, in Maurice's favorite chair. This surely meant that the guest was more than ordinarily important. Georgie was smiling, fluttering, fanning herself, apologizing for the warm weather. Maurice jumped up to light the gentleman's cigar. The center of all the attention seemed to Ethel singularly unimpressive. He was a young man whose eyes were circled with such dark shadows that they seemed smudged with coal dust. He was shuffling through a pile of papers that Ethel recognized as being in Maurice's handwriting.

The young man drew deeply on his cigar, then turned to Maurice, who was leaning forward expectantly. "Yes, I've had the chance to read the manuscript, and I think it would play well. I suggest you send it to Miss Bernhardt. If she could be persuaded to play the leading role, the production would be assured success," the visitor said.

"Do you really think so, Mr. Wilde?" Georgie asked.

The man named Wilde chuckled pleasantly. "If your husband weren't quite so handsome, he'd make a great playwright and give me quite too much competition. I hope the public won't let him give up his acting career."

Maurice assumed a look of unaccustomed modesty. "It's pleasant to hear this from you, Oscar," he said, "but of course you exaggerate. Yet having passed the first critical test, I wish to propose a toast in something stronger than tea. Ethel, bring the tray over there."

Ethel turned to the sideboard with its silver tray, on which were arranged a decanter and two thin-stemmed glasses. She cautiously picked up the tray and edged toward the table beside her father. She focused her eyes on the floor so she wouldn't have to glance at the stranger.

"Look up, Pauline, look up," Georgie said, using a line from *The Lady of Lyons*. Georgie used it as a reminder to the bashful Ethel that she should keep her head high and smile.

Ethel tried to follow directions, but as she raised her head the first thing she saw was Oscar Wilde, his black-circled eyes looking like the hollows of a death mask. Ethel let out a cry of terror, dropped the tray, and fled the room.

Ethel's departure ended the tea hour abruptly. It was no time at all before both Georgie and Maurice entered Ethel's bedroom, where she was hiding her head under a pillow, too frightened to cry.

It was Georgie who was shedding the tears. "How could you, Ethel? Haven't we taught you proper courtesies?"

"Forget the words," Maurice interrupted. "This is a time for the Green Slipper."

Ethel knew what that meant. The slipper was made of soft Russian leather, and when administered by Maurice's firm hand, it caused more noise than pain. Still, it was reserved for only the most awful crimes, and the humiliation was severe. Ethel endured the punishment, still without tears, which infuriated Maurice. But the lecture had been given and there was nothing more to be said, so they left Ethel alone to reflect on her disastrous behavior. The solitude was precious. She enjoyed a day of self-pity.

Although Lionel, Ethel, and John had few friends in London, Polly made up for the loss. She had been hired as a nurse for little John, but she tucked all three children under her wing. Polly was a handsome girl with red, crinkly hair. Maurice said she looked like Mary Anderson, the actress, only prettier. Ethel immediately fell in love with pretty Polly, entranced with her strange way of twisting words. At first

Ethel was sure Polly was speaking a foreign language, yet by listening carefully she could usually untangle Polly's meaning. Lionel laughed when Ethel started to copy some of Polly's speech.

"You sound just like a limey Britisher," Lionel mocked.

Polly had been instructed to show the children the historic landmarks of London. "It's such an easy way to take care of their education," said Georgie.

Polly was pleased with her assignment, which gave her a chance to see many sights for the first time herself. She planned one such excursion to Madame Tussaud's Wax Works. As Polly said, "You'll learn what's in the schoolbooks there. And as our history is a bit thicker than yours, it's best to find a way to learn it in a hurry."

Ethel was delighted with the idea, but Lionel groaned. Any form of education, no matter how painless, depressed him. John, who was to go along because Cook was busy, didn't know which side to take. Maurice gave Polly some money for the day's expenses without bothering to inquire just what activities Polly had planned. As usual, he was overly generous, but at the museum Polly argued over the price of admission for John and saved a few coins for herself. Soon they entered a darkened room.

The very first figure, Lord Cromwell, terrified Ethel. Every detail of his face had been carefully molded in wax, then painted in lifelike color. His wig was tinged with gray. The buttons of his uniform were polished, yet there was a certain bagginess at the knees of his trousers, as if he had just risen. The gaslight flickered against his veined hands. The wax figure looked unbelievably real, but Cromwell somehow did not look alive.

Lionel put her thoughts into words. "He looks as if he just stepped out of his coffin."

Ethel squealed in terror and buried her face in Polly's skirt.

"Now there's nothing to be crying about," Polly said impatiently. "He's made just like one of your dolls. Look."

Reluctantly Ethel obeyed, but the second glance was just as bad. She longed to leave this terrible place. Lionel, who hadn't wanted to come in the first place, couldn't be dragged away. He was fascinated. Polly managed to urge him along only when she told him they'd miss the grand tour of the dungeon if they didn't hurry. Polly read the words of a large sign in front of them: "To the Chamber of Horrors — On Display — Every Machine of Torture Ever Used in the British and Continental Penal Systems — Absolutely Authentic."

A guide was now gathering a crowd around him. Ethel was shoved and pushed until she felt panicky. There was nowhere to run. Blindly she followed Polly, afraid of getting lost in this dreadful place. They made their way down a narrow, winding flight of stairs. The walls on either side had been built of stone, kept suitably wet and slimy to the touch. The air had a green, dank odor, except at one end where a fire had been built under a copper cauldron to produce more misery for the waxen prisoners about to be tortured.

Ethel kept her eyes shut, but she couldn't block out the voice of the guide, who was dramatically detailing every gory item of British history. Even Polly seemed to be looking around for a place to rest, but they were forced to stand until the guide's last sentence was delivered.

Little John had been unable to see anything, being buried in the crowd. Now that the audience was thinning, he grabbed hold of one of the chains anchored firmly to the stone wall. He liked the sound of the noisy rattle. Polly yanked him by the hand to hurry him along. John screamed in disappointment. Ethel could stand it no longer; she burst into tears. Now even Polly was weeping. She lunged forward, dragging Ethel and John with her, shouting to Lionel to hurry.

"You babies should be locked in the nursery," Lionel taunted.

The thought of being locked up anywhere drove Ethel into deeper fright. That night she was afraid to shut her eyes, and when they finally did close with exhaustion, she relived every detail of the horrible scenes in the wax museum.

Even Georgie noticed Ethel's tenseness the next morning. "Why, whatever is wrong, dear?" she asked.

Suddenly the tears that had stopped flowing hours before flooded Ethel's eyes again.

"She's still scared of the dungeon," Lionel answered.

"The *what?*" asked their mother.

"Polly took us to see the wax dolls yesterday, and we saw the Chamber of Horrors. It was great. I want to go again," Lionel reported.

"That's hardly the place for children your age. I will speak to Polly about that," said Georgie. Then, hugging Ethel's trembling shoulders, she smiled and said, "But they were only make-believe, Ethel, just like play-acting on the stage."

"No," wailed Ethel, "it was all true."

"Now, that's enough. You'll ruin your eyes, and today you want to look your best. Remember, you are going to a birthday party," said Georgie.

Ethel had forgotten, and she wished Georgie had, too. Last week Lady Teasle, whom Georgie admired a great deal, had sent her footman to the Barrymore residence with a written note inviting Ethel and Lionel to her son's birthday party. Ethel had met Philip Teasle only once. He was eight, but tall for his age, with knobby knees and red hair that stuck out from around his ears like wisps of straw.

"Do I have to go?" Ethel asked.

"Of course you do," Georgie said. "You'll have such fun, and you can wear your new white dress with the blue bow."

This was the only cheerful thought, for Ethel loved to dress up in party clothes. Georgie had had a dressmaker make almost a copy of one of her own ball gowns for Ethel. The skirt was made of rows of organdy ruffles; the narrow waist was tied with a wide blue sash.

But Lionel was furious about his costume. Georgie had purchased for him a blue velvet suit with a wide lace collar and knee breeches that tucked into white silk stockings. His black party pumps had silver buckles.

"I'm not going!" he shouted.

One more time Maurice was called upon to administer the Green Slipper. Finally the two young Barrymores were dressed and ready to go.

As soon as they arrived, Ethel realized that Georgie had overindulged her love of fashion. No other little girls wore quite as many ruffles or petticoats, and none of the boys were wearing robin's-egg blue velvet. Lionel refused to take part in any games and remained in the pantry until refreshments were served. Ethel tried to hide in a corner, but Lady Teasle kindly saved the day by introducing her to a somber-faced little girl who seemed equally ill at ease.

"Evangeline, maybe Ethel will tell you about her pet monkey."

"Do you have a real monkey?" Evangeline asked in awe.

Ethel nodded. "Yes, we call her Eleanora." It was Maurice who collected the strange animals. Ethel hardly ever went out to the garden to play with them.

"Could I come and see her, please?" Evangeline asked.

"Yes, and you can see the possum and the peacock, too," said Ethel.

By this time a group of guests had gathered. Ethel began to lose her shyness. She was sorry when Polly arrived to take them home. She had had a good time after all, but Lionel's humiliation was still to come. The young host announced in mocking falsetto tones, "Lionel, you're fetched."

Lionel attacked in a fury and pushed Master Philip into the lily bed. The host got to his feet and swung wildly at Lionel. Two servants dragged the boys apart, but in the melee Lionel's blue velvet suit was ripped at the sleeve. He was led home in disgrace. Certainly the Green Slipper would be used again.

Surprisingly, when Maurice returned home before supper and was told of the fight, he smiled and asked to hear Lionel describe the scene himself. Then he laughed uproariously.

"Maurice, you have been drinking," Georgie accused. "Your eyes — there's something wrong with your eyes."

"Yes, they will both be iridescently black by tomorrow, my dear," Maurice proclaimed. "But I will wear these shiners as a badge of distinction. I have just come from the Rainer Street Gymnasium, where I have floored the heavyweight champion of Great Britain in a boxing bout. Perhaps Lionel has inherited some of my skill."

"Maurice, how can you say such a thing?" Georgie demanded. "Lady Teasle will never invite us to her home again. And besides, Lionel's suit is ruined."

"I commend Lionel's behavior," said Maurice. "Torn velvet can always be mended; honor, never."

With these ringing words, the subject was dropped, and no one ever saw the beautiful, blue velvet suit again.

Georgie and Maurice Barrymore continued to receive invitations to the gayest parties in London, even to the home of the Teasles, but it became apparent that they were not entertaining at home as lavishly as before. The inheritance had come to an end; Maurice accepted two roles at the Haymarket Theatre. One was in *Diplomacy*, by Sardou, the other in *A Woman of No Importance*, written by Maurice's friend Oscar Wilde.

Still, it was not long before the family finances were strained beyond repair. Rather than show themselves destitute before their British friends, Maurice made the decision that the Barrymores would return to America.

"Madame Modjeska is arranging another tour. We are going home," he said.

4

Going home didn't mean exactly that for Ethel. On the trip back it was decided that she would be sent to the Academy of Notre Dame in Philadelphia.

"Six years is young, but she is tall," Maurice commented, not very logically.

"Oh, please, Maurice, I would much rather stay with you and Georgie or Grandmother," Ethel pleaded.

"No, it's time someone in the family became familiar with the inside of a book," said Maurice. "Lionel will be enrolled at Mount Saint Vincent on the Hudson. One good thing about your mother's conversion — Catholics have the best boarding schools."

Tears spilled silently down Ethel's cheeks, but Georgie had no patience with sadness. "Smile, Ethel, smile. It will be such fun being with girls your own age. And maybe you'll like the piano. That's always nice," she added.

Ethel's suitcase and Ethel were promptly delivered to the convent on Rittenhouse Square. She was met on the steps by Sister Julie de Saint Esprit, the mistress of the boarders. Sister Julie's smile helped steady Ethel's trembling knees.

"We're glad you're here, Ethel. It's almost supper time.

You may take your suitcase to the dormitory and tidy up for the bell. I'll show you the way."

"Yes, m'um," said Ethel, giving a touch of a British accent even to this short speech.

"Here we are called Sister," the nun said gently. "It won't take long before you get used to our ways."

Ethel thought that she could never feel at home in this strange place, with its black-robed nuns gliding about silently. The corridor ahead reached like a long, frightening tunnel into the interior of the old building. An endless row of doors, closed at this time of day, slotted the hallway in deep shadows. The floor squeaked as Ethel and Sister Julie climbed the stairs.

Ethel heard a muffled hum of voices, broken every now and then by laughter, but when Sister Julie opened the door to the first-form sleeping hall, a wave of silence rolled across the room. Then, almost in unison, the girls bounced a curtsy and murmured, "Good evening, Sister."

Ethel glanced around the room at the staring faces, each looking identical in spite of braids or curls or freckles or clear, pink cheeks — identical because all the girls wore navy pleated skirts and high-necked blouses. Quickly Ethel looked down at the toes of her shoes. As if from a distance, she heard Sister Julie de Saint Esprit answer the girls' greetings. "Good evening. We have a new girl for this form. Her name is Ethel Barrymore. She will have the bed next to yours, Mary."

When Mary touched Ethel's hand to take the suitcase, Ethel drew back, then looked up to the friendly face of a dark-haired girl with heavy braids over each shoulder.

"I'll put it over here with mine," said Mary.

"That's all right. I can manage."

"*Mahnage?* Where did you learn to talk like that?" asked a short, plump girl standing by the nearest bed.

Sister Julie helped the flustered Ethel by explaining, "Ethel has spent some time in England with her parents. I'm sure before the week goes by we will hear a bit of London rubbing off on Philadelphia and vice versa."

"You sound so grand," said Mary.

Suddenly a very loud bell jangled in the hallway, and everyone rushed for the door. Sister Julie clapped her hands together just once, and immediately there was quiet. "Ethel will be the first in line this evening," she said.

"I'm not really hungry," said Ethel.

"Don't be absurd," said Sister Julie. "Of course you're hungry."

She took Ethel firmly by the hand and led her once more into the hallway. Other doors had now opened, and groups of older girls, all in the same uniform, joined Ethel's group in an orderly procession to the dining room on the first floor.

Long trestle tables filled the room. Ethel was seated with the younger girls at one of the far tables. Mary edged in beside her, and the two girls smiled shyly at each other. Sister Julie sat at the head of the table. As soon as the blessing was said, the girls started chattering about the spring concert and music recital scheduled for the following week.

"We're going to march in first," said Mary.

"And we're all going to wear white dresses and carry a flower and a candle. Do you have one?" asked Amelia, the girl across the table.

"One what?" asked Ethel.

"A white dress. We all must have one."

Ethel nodded. "I have a white dress I wore to a birthday party last year."

There was a wave of giggles. "You do sound grand," Mary repeated.

Ethel's face flushed. She was careful not to speak again

during the meal. When she was back in the dormitory, she unfastened her suitcase to hang up the few dresses she had been allowed to bring with her.

"Oh, let's see the white one," said Amelia.

Slowly Ethel unfolded the crinkly paper in which Polly had wrapped the layers of white ruffles. A chorus of "Oohs" sounded around her. Ethel smiled with pride.

"It's beautiful," said Mary. "It's a real grown-up dress."

"It's just like Georgie's," said Ethel.

"Who is Georgie?"

"My mother," Ethel answered.

"Why do you call her by her first name?" asked Amelia. Ethel frowned. "I always have."

"I'd get a switching if I called a grown-up by her first name," said Amelia, "but then I know who your mother is. She's an actress."

"She plays on the stage?" another girl asked. Now everyone crowded around. The questions came one after another.

"Does she wear costumes and makeup?"

"Does she talk funny like you?"

"My mother says no nice girl would ever be on the stage," said Amelia.

Ethel felt angry and confused. Tears burned her eyes, but she answered quickly, "My mother and father and my grandmother and my aunts and uncles are all on the stage, and they are all famous because they are the greatest actors in the world. It even said so in the paper." The tears stopped before they could spill, and Ethel raised her chin high.

"Forget about Amelia," said Mary. "She just wishes her family were famous. Put on the dress, Ethel, and let's see."

Ethel pulled off her wool dress, then carefully slipped on three petticoats before she put on the party gown.

Mary caught her breath. "You look just like a princess."

The door opened, and again there was silence as Sister Julie entered. "That is very pretty, Ethel," she said, "but I think you had better put it away now. You'll have your uniform in the morning."

"But this is her white dress to wear for the recital," said Mary. "We will all be wearing white."

"I don't think this is quite suitable," said Sister Julie, "but we will see that Ethel has something to wear. I'm sure I can find a simpler dress."

Again Ethel felt confused and hurt. Why wasn't her dress suitable? Why did the girls think that she talked differently, when she felt that it was everyone else who was strange? Right now she wished she were back with Georgie or with Mum mum, who would certainly know how to answer them.

"It's time for bed now," Sister Julie continued. "Lights must be out in five minutes."

Even this statement was strange. At home she sometimes stayed up until midnight because she always had to be quiet in the morning. Ethel pulled her nightgown out of her suitcase and put the white party gown back in its folds of tissue. There was a scent of violets from one of Georgie's handkerchiefs. Ethel pressed it close to her face and slipped between the sheets of her hard bed, closing her eyes and wishing sleep would come right away. Instead, she stayed awake listening to the strange noises of a squeaking cot, a cough, the living sounds of twenty girls all around her. Ethel put the pillow over her head. It was damp with tears, but she finally fell asleep.

A bell jangled her awake in the morning. Sister Superior Agnes Mary came into the dormitory room carrying both a uniform and a white dress.

"We'll see how these fit, little Ethel," she said kindly. "If there's any alteration, I'll come back with pins and scissors myself."

"Maurice says I'm tall for my age," said Ethel.

"I'm sure you are, dear. It's just that you are the youngest in the school, and I had quite forgotten sizes."

The white dress hung limply, unattractively, almost to the floor. Even after it was pulled in and up with a sash, it obviously did not fit. Ethel made up her mind that she would never wear it, no matter what anybody told her. On schedule, she developed a violent coughing spasm the morning of the spring concert. Sister Julie was summoned, and it was decided that Ethel might spoil the program for everyone if she attended. She was tucked into bed and given a spoonful of horrid-tasting medicine, which she swallowed bravely, willingly.

The aspects of her personality that set Ethel apart from her classmates also helped her to make friends. Except for Amelia, the girls were thrilled at the thought that Ethel's mother and father were on the stage. They continued their questions: "How do actors memorize all their lines? Are the costumes of silk and satin? Are the jewels real?"

During recess the older girls sat Ethel on a bench and asked her about all the famous stage people she must know. Her audience seemed delighted no matter what answers she gave, because of her British way of speaking. Although Ethel's white dress with the ruffles was never worn, everyone stopped by to see it. In spite of her shyness, Ethel was surrounded by curious friends.

Ethel saw her family occasionally. Most often it was Mummum who dropped by, always with a little surprise tucked in her pocket — never sweets, but sometimes a length of ribbon for Ethel's hair or a bottle of fragrance. Maurice came once to take his daughter to a baseball game. And of course there were summer vacations when the whole family gathered: Ethel's mother, father, and brothers, Uncle Sidney and Aunt Gladys, and, of course, Mum mum.

Ethel would always remember a wonderful summer she spent on Staten Island when she was eight. She wrote in her diary in 1887 that she learned to swim that year and spent hours diving through the giant breakers. Georgie would race all three of her children down the beach, calling out, "Come along, kids, lunch."

Mum mum pretended to be shocked. "Children are not kids, Georgie. How will they ever learn proper ways if you don't grow up yourself?"

But Georgie would laugh. "As long as there's no audience, I won't grow up."

That summer Ethel grew an inch taller. She had her hair bobbed in bangs, in spite of Maurice's disapproval. Her suntan was dotted with so many mosquito bites that Lionel called her "Miss Leopard Child" or "Miss Water Rat." Ethel hated to think of returning to school, but finally it was time for the family to separate, and once more bags were packed and uniforms put in order.

The only thing Ethel really missed when she was not at Notre Dame was her music lessons. She had been thrilled from the first moment she sat at the big upright piano, her feet dangling from the stool. Sister Aloysius had placed her fingers on the keys and had shown Ethel how to play a seven-note scale. Even this mechanical sound was exciting. On the first day, Sister Aloysius rearranged a few notes, and a tune took shape. It was "Twinkle, Twinkle, Little Star." Ethel repeated the pattern of notes, playing the tune over and over.

Sister Aloysius smiled. "That's fine, Ethel, but to keep Sister Julie from stuffing cotton in her ears, we will give you another tune to learn, one that is written in this book. See how the notes tell you what to do."

From that day on, Ethel spent all of her free time in the practice room. Sister Aloysius was a strict teacher, a perfectionist who was hard to please, but Ethel was in love with music. She was happiest at the piano, and she soon became one of Sister's best pupils.

Ethel won a silver medal in the school's recital playing Beethoven's Sonata No. 13. But Mary Heizmann, Ethel's friend, received first prize for "Nearer My God to Thee" with variations, and Ethel was crushed.

Mum mum had been there to hear her, and Mrs. Drew was sympathetic. "You were excellent, Ethel, but, after all, the subject of Mary's piece was a bit more to Sister's liking."

"No, it was the way Mary played it. I'll try harder next time," Ethel said.

Sister Aloysius herself was pleased with Ethel's talent. She wrote a letter to Mr. and Mrs. Barrymore suggesting that their daughter be given further musical training and insisting that Maurice must come to the academy to hear his daughter play.

Maurice arrived reluctantly, upset that he must waste his time listening to other students who were performing first. He fidgeted through a violin solo and finally left the room to pace up and down in the corridor. When he returned, Ethel was halfway through her piece. Before she finished, he had suddenly changed. There were tears in his eyes. When she stopped playing, he stood and clapped. "Vienna, Leschetizky! She must go!" he cried.

Ethel was thrilled. Maybe she would have a chance to become a concert pianist. She was never nervous or tense when she sat before a piano in front of an audience. Yet if she had to memorize anything for recitation, she suffered agonizing stage fright. Reciting words was not her talent, Ethel felt, but music was different. It would be her career.

The school terms passed, one by one. When she wasn't practicing her piano lessons, Ethel buried herself in books. *Alice in Wonderland* was her first favorite. Then she discovered the excitement of *Kidnapped, The Prisoner of Zenda,* and the works of Scott and Robert Elsmere.

Lionel teased her about being "Little Miss Bookworm." John marveled, "You really like school? You are absolutely crazy, but then, if you don't want to be an actor, I guess you've got to do something."

Ethel continued her studies at the convent until she was thirteen. Then she received an urgent note from her father, saying that she was to come to New York to be with Georgie, who was ill. Bronchitis, he said.

5

Ethel tried to hide the shock she felt when she first saw her mother in New York. When Ethel entered the hotel room, Georgie was leaning over an enormous trunk, trying to shove an extra pair of brocade slippers into a corner already wedged tight with other belongings. When she straightened up and turned, Georgie's face was flushed, and she was breathing heavily. Even under a layer of powder, shadows hollowed her cheeks, and her eyes told the real story of her health. When she saw Ethel, she hurried across the room, forcing a bit of familiar gaiety into her voice.

"Ethel, dear, I could hardly wait for you to get here. I'm going through one of my impatient stages. Maurice told me you couldn't possibly have received the letter before last week. But here you are, and everything is right again," Georgie cooed.

"How are you?" Ethel asked anxiously.

"I'm fine — oh, a slight case of bronchitis, but that is why I've sent for you, dear," her mother answered. "We have the most exciting trip planned. The doctor thinks I would recover more quickly if I could find a spot of sunshine, and as neither New York nor Philadelphia seems to hold much promise of that, I've decided to go to California."

"California?" Ethel repeated with surprise.

"Yes, isn't that grand? And as I couldn't stand to think of a train trip, Maurice has booked passage by ship. The only time we will have to board one of those awful cinder-filled carriages is when we cross the Isthmus of Panama."

"Will Maurice be coming, too?" Ethel asked.

"No, he could never leave the tour for that long. He's practicing Shakespeare again. He really looks much better in a tailcoat, but then they seem to have written better parts for him a few centuries ago." Georgie laughed merrily, and for a moment the lines of fatigue were erased from her face, but the laughter brought on a spasm of coughing. She sat on the edge of her bed, trying to catch her breath.

"Can I get you something?" Ethel asked anxiously.

"Not a thing. It's just a nuisance of a tickle that the doctor guarantees will be cured by the climate," Georgie said after a moment. "Now, you're just in time to help me finish packing."

Ethel looked around her and was surprised to see not just one trunk but three others overflowing with beautiful silks and satins. "Will you be needing all of these, Georgie? How long will we be gone?" asked Ethel.

"I haven't the faintest idea, but I am going to take everything, even my ball gowns. Mr. and Mrs. Simpson — he's the mayor of Santa Barbara — are already planning a party for us when we arrive."

Ethel busied herself folding and packing the last of the clothing scattered around the room. Maurice came in as the last trunk was closed.

"It's good to see my two girls together again." His voice was soft with tenderness, strange compared with his usual blustering way. "I've ordered your favorite dinner, wild duck and champagne. We'll have it served here in the room."

"Oh, Maurice, how thoughtful," Georgie exclaimed. "This packing has tired me more than I suspected. Tonight I don't want to dress for an audience in the dining room."

A steward wheeled in the party fare and placed it on a small table set with linen, silver, and candles. For the first time in Ethel's memory, she alone shared dinner with her parents. She watched them as they smiled at each other and tried to keep up a light conversation about the events of the day. No one mentioned their parting.

Georgie rose as soon as the flaming cherries were finished. "You won't mind my retiring early this evening, Maurice, will you? We'll have an early start in the morning, and you know I'm not used to that."

"Not at all, my dear. I'll see you then." Very formally, he kissed her hand.

Ethel and Maurice left the room together. In the hall Ethel turned to ask her father the important question. "Is she really very sick?"

"Of course not." Maurice sounded confident. "She is tired, overworked. I should have insisted that she give up traveling with the company long ago. After all, she is thirty-four, not a young ingenue anymore. But then she always points to her mother, the indomitable Mrs. Drew, and insists that she will equal her record. Sunshine and rest will take care of her maladies."

Ethel did not answer.

"I would not let you leave on such a trip, Ethel, if I thought there were any danger," her father added.

Maurice's sincere tone of voice at once calmed Ethel's nerves. That night she dreamed of a sea voyage under tropical skies.

Maurice was the only one at the pier to see them off the next day. Lionel and John were in school; Mrs. Drew was

traveling again with *The Rivals*. Georgie was wearing a hya-
cinth-blue jacket above a matching bustled skirt. She had
decorated her tiny hat with a nosegay of flowers that Maurice had brought her as a "trifling departure gift," he said.

Suddenly Georgie flung her arms around her husband's
neck and buried her face on his shoulder. "Don't forget me,
Maurice," she whispered.

"I will be joining you before the season is over," he assured
her.

"And you will bring the boys?" Georgie asked.

"Of course, if you can bear that much family all at once."
He bent to kiss Georgie's cheek, where the tears had begun
to fall.

Ethel was frightened. "Oh, please, Maurice, you come,
too."

"A fine scene this makes, two hysterical women bound on
a pleasure cruise," he commented.

A deep-throated blast from the ship's horn interrupted the
farewells. Maurice turned toward the gangway and disappeared into the crowd on the dock, but Ethel could see
him waving his top hat. The lines were cast off, and a snub-
prowed tug was already nudging the big ship away from the
pier. Ethel turned to say something to Georgie, but she
wasn't there. For a moment Ethel felt panic, then realized
her mother must have left for the stateroom.

Ethel had to ask directions. She followed a white-coated
steward down a narrow companionway to berth 16 C. Ethel
knocked lightly, but the door was not locked. As she stepped
up and over the threshold, she collided with one of the
trunks. Georgie was lying down on the berth.

"Are you all right, Georgie?"

"Yes, just weary," her mother answered. "Why don't you

go up on deck for a while? I'll rest before we sort out the confusion." She waved her hand at the trunks and valises.

Ethel turned to go, but she felt shy about mingling with the passengers by herself. She returned in about an hour. Georgie had put on one of her lovely dressing gowns and was back in bed, this time sound asleep. There was no need to unpack now.

It was another full day before Ethel bothered to unpack a change of clothing for herself. She was worried that Georgie seemed so exhausted, but she told herself that this was exactly what the doctor had advised — rest and a change of climate. Ethel ordered their meals served in their cabin.

"You shouldn't be staying in this stuffy room with me. Go meet people, Ethel," Georgie said.

"I'd rather not," Ethel answered.

On the third day Georgie seemed to be much stronger. When she woke in the morning, she gave Ethel orders to unpack half a dozen outfits from the smallest trunk. Ethel helped arrange her mother's hair and watched Georgie rub "just a smudge of pink" rouge on her cheeks.

"I'm feeling better already," Georgie said. "Is it warm enough for my pink dimity?" She didn't wait for an answer. "Yes, I feel like pink today. Dear, please help me with my laces. What would I do without you?"

Ethel fumbled with the corset ties but noticed that Mama had lost so much weight that her stays were quite loose. Yet she looked lovely. Ethel was at once proud and jealous of having such a beautiful mother. It made her own appearance seem drab. What could she do with her straight, colorless hair, her bulging eyes? She was tall for her age but not quite grown-up enough to wear her dresses to the floor. They hung at an awkward length above her high-button shoes and the black cotton stockings that had seemed so right at the convent, but not on shipboard heading into the tropics.

Georgie noticed the stockings and frowned. "I think you'll be too warm in those, Ethel. Here, try on a pair of mine."

She handed Ethel a lovely pair of sand-colored silk stockings. Ethel put them on. They were smooth and soft. "I'll never wear cotton again," she said.

Georgie agreed. "You are almost a young lady." Then she added, "Not quite, of course, but think of yourself as one anyway. It helps the posture."

When Georgie and Ethel Barrymore appeared in the grand salon for lunch, they were warmly greeted by many passengers who were strangers. Many knew Georgie by sight as a famous actress; those who did not were charmed by her beauty and smile.

The weather was warm. They spent their days stretched in deck chairs enjoying the warm breeze that smelled of fish and sunshine. The sea sparkled around them and laid itself smoothly across their path. The ship stopped at several ports along the Mexican coast, but the sleepy villages and smelly docks did not lure them ashore. By the time they reached Panama, they were both suntanned.

Georgie was happy, and Ethel forgot her worries, forgot the moments of concern she felt when she heard her mother cough and turn restlessly in her sleep.

Again, Ethel packed and locked the trunks. This time they were stowed in the baggage car of the little train that was to take Georgie and Ethel across the Isthmus of Panama to another ship in the Pacific. In places along the way, the engine brushed aside dense undergrowth that threatened to choke the path of the train. The conductor with the handlebar moustache pointed out the great, deserted machines that the Frenchman de Lesseps had used in his unsuccessful attempt to gouge a passageway through the jungle.

The blue Pacific did not live up to its peaceful name. Only hours after Ethel and Georgie boarded the small ship that was to take them up the western coast, a fresh wind piled the waves into froth-tipped mountains. Everyone stayed below decks — everyone except Georgie and Ethel. Georgie would not think of missing the excitement of the storm. The wind on her face seemed to give her more strength than the healing sun.

When the ship landed at Santa Barbara, California, Georgie and Ethel were the only passengers to disembark. Georgie embraced plump Mrs. Bosworth, whom she had known on shipboard for less than a week, with the same affection she had for the Simpsons, who were on the pier to greet her and her daughter.

The mayor of Santa Barbara was a short little man whose wife towered at least three inches above his balding pate. Their daughter, just Ethel's age, was as tall as her mother.

The mayor pushed the girl forward gently. "This is Mabel. You two girls should get to know each other, that is, if you can get Mabel to talk a bit." Mayor Simpson laughed. "Shy as a mouse most of the time, but once you get her started on her favorite subject, caterpillars — imagine, caterpillars! — she'll lecture the rest of the day."

"Please, Papa." Mabel blushed. "It's butterflies."

"Same thing." The mayor laughed even louder. Then, turning to Georgie, he explained, "I've arranged to have your luggage taken to the Arlington Hotel."

"We're so sorry," Mrs. Simpson interrupted, "but our house is full of relatives at the moment."

"Your relatives, my dear," the mayor added. Then he

went on, "But tomorrow you can look at a house that is available at a very nominal rental. I did not want to take the liberty of moving you in without your approval."

"I don't know whether we will need a house," said Georgie.

"We intend to make you a permanent resident of Santa Barbara, Mrs. Barrymore," Mayor Simpson said, "an honorary resident."

Both Georgie and Ethel were delighted with the cottage. The front porch was almost entirely closed in by a fragrant wall of roses that climbed the roof and even poured into the windows. Georgie and Ethel moved into the house the day after their arrival in Santa Barbara. Georgie hired a Chinese cook, but Ethel took charge of the household. She felt proud that her mother considered her equal to the responsibilities. In the last few weeks of travel they had become closer than ever before, and Georgie was no longer just the distant celebrity darting in and out of Ethel's schoolgirl life. They had a chance to talk both of the past and the future, although nothing was ever said of Georgie's illness.

Georgie admitted that she hated the thought of giving up her stage career. It had opened so many doors for her to meet exciting people; even the President of the United States, Grover Cleveland, had invited her for a sail on his yacht. Ethel had never quite realized what a famous person her own mother was. Yet Georgie wasn't always talking about herself. She was interested in Ethel's shy mention that she hoped to be a concert pianist and promised to write letters to friends abroad to inquire about Ethel's studying in Europe — sometime in the future, of course, when Ethel was older.

It had been a wonderful month of travel, and now Ethel and her mother were settling down to spend even more time together. Ethel was the happiest she had ever been. For the first few days she bustled around the four rooms of the cottage, unpacking the lovely clothes. Georgie, of course, had a letter to the doctor who was going to make her well, so on one of their first outings they went to his office. Ethel noticed that Georgie fidgeted nervously with her handkerchief while they were in the carriage.

"You will stay with me, Ethel, won't you?" she asked.

Ethel was surprised. "Of course, Georgie," she said.

Even when Georgie was admitted to the doctor's office, while he was listening to her chest and hearing her cough, Ethel stayed close by. He looked grave, but then all doctors looked that way, Ethel told herself.

"And who is to take care of you, Mrs. Barrymore?" he asked.

"My little girl."

"You have no nurse?" he asked.

Georgie shook her head. "No, I don't want a nurse, just my little girl."

Ethel was frightened.

"I want it to be just the two of us," Georgie continued, "though we aren't really alone. We have friends."

And they did have friends. The house was busy with callers. Sometimes Mabel came with her mother for tea. The mayor had been wrong. His daughter loved to talk, especially when she and Ethel were in the garden alone.

Mabel confided that she wanted to be a writer. "Not just to write about pretend things, but real things."

"Butterflies, maybe?" Ethel asked.

"Don't laugh. Yes, I do want to write about butterflies and nature. I'm going to study it all in school. What are you going to do?"

"I want to be a concert pianist," said Ethel. She paused,

then went on, "But I don't know whether I'm good enough or not."

"Oh, Ethel, that would be wonderful," said Mabel with enthusiasm. "You can come to our house to play the piano, maybe this Sunday. Mama and Papa are taking your mother for a drive in the country."

"I'd like that," Ethel answered.

But that day Ethel suddenly changed her mind. It seemed such a long time since she had been at the convent, since she had enjoyed the solemn dignity of a darkened church. "I think I will go to Mass," she told her mother.

"Of course," Georgie agreed. "That is a fine idea."

Ethel was glad she had decided to go. The church with its thick adobe walls was not at all like the Gothic chapel at Notre Dame Convent, but it had the familiar hush of worship, the smell of incense and candles.

On the way home, Ethel walked slowly, enjoying the quiet around her, the strange trees and flowers she had never seen growing in the East, the long vines that climbed the walls. She was in no hurry, for Georgie would probably not return for another hour.

Mabel interrupted Ethel's daydreams, exclaiming, "Oh, Ethel, hurry home! Your mother has had a hemorrhage."

Ethel ran with the wind, yet she felt that only her heart must be racing. When she got there, the little house was full of neighbors, some of whom she had never seen before. The doctor was sitting next to Georgie's bed. Georgie's face was ashen. Suddenly she wrenched forward to cough and struggle for breath. Perspiration beaded her forehead.

"Oh, Georgie, Georgie," Ethel sobbed.

The doctor spoke very quietly. "There is nothing more we can do. Let your mother rest. I will call you if there is any change."

Numbness crept through Ethel's mind, through her body. She turned to leave the room in a daze. Mrs. Simpson rushed forward to put her arms around Ethel. "Dear, there's nothing to worry about," she said.

But Ethel knew this wasn't true. "I must call for a priest," she said mechanically. Her words sounded strange. It didn't seem possible her mother could be dying, not when she had been so cheerful this morning, but somehow Ethel knew.

"Mabel has already gone to the church, dear. Stay here with us," said Mrs. Simpson.

At that moment, a young man in black robes hurried through the doorway. Ethel stayed outside the room as her mother was given the last rites of the church. After the priest was finished, Ethel went inside and held her mother's frail hand. Ethel stood very still and dry-eyed.

"You must save your strength, young woman," the doctor said. "Sit down and rest." Ethel did not hear him.

Within an hour, Georgie Barrymore, beautiful, talented, witty young actress and mother, was dead. Ethel did not cry. There was no time for that, not yet. Ethel was thirteen years old, alone in a strange city. First she sent telegrams to Maurice and to Uncle Sidney Drew, who would know how to break the news to Mum mum and the boys. She made plans with the undertaker to take Georgie's body back on the train to New York. There was no money for mourning clothes, so she put up her hair, as a proper young woman should, and wore her convent uniform. Georgie's clothes were packed and taken to the station.

For four nights and four days, Ethel sat in the day coach, looking at, but not seeing, the scenery flashing by the window. Her father met her in Chicago, but he was no help at all. His mood alternated between hysterical weeping and blank silence.

"What will we do now?" she asked. He had no answers.

Ethel took charge of having the casket transferred to the eastern train. In New York, Grandmother Drew was at the station to meet them. Ethel fell into Mum mum's arms. This time they were strong arms. Mrs. Drew made the final plans for the funeral service. Although Georgie had joined the Catholic church, the services were held at St. Stephen's Episcopal Church in Philadelphia.

The church was thronged with friends and strangers. Ethel walked beside her father; Lionel took Aunt Gladys's arm. John was sick in bed. On the ride to Glenwood Cemetery, Ethel kept saying to herself, "It's not true. It's not true." She had just come to know her mother, and to lose Georgie so soon was cruelly unfair.

The convent seemed her only security. Ethel returned for another semester of school.

6

Two important things happened that year, 1893. Ethel read in the paper that her father had remarried. He had not called or written to tell her the news. Suddenly Ethel realized that she must take over the management of family matters. Handsome, talented Maurice was too irresponsible or uncaring to bother with them now.

Ethel's first decision was that her brother John should be baptized a Catholic as Georgie would have wished. Ethel found a boy at Mount Saint Vincent who consented to be John's godfather. Ethel, as godmother, stood at John's side, feeling a bit like Saint Paul, but looking like a solemn little girl in hair ribbons.

Before Ethel finished her term at the convent, she was sent for by her Grandmother Drew, who was touring in Canada in *The Rivals*. Mum mum's letter was brief but filled with more unexpected news. She had not been able to meet the expenses of the Arch Street Theater and so had given up her lease and taken her group of players on tour. Mrs. Drew's letter stated that it was time for Ethel to earn her own living, and so it was necessary for Ethel to join them in Montreal.

The fact that Ethel had never acted on the stage in her life and that she still clung to the hope of a career as a concert pianist made no difference. Ethel did as she was told, said goodbye to her friends, and packed her small trunk with her convent uniforms and the few possessions she had saved that had belonged to her mother: a cameo brooch, a black velvet cape, and one pair of brocade slippers that were a size too small for her.

Ethel stood on the railroad platform, looking every bit as forlorn as she felt. Her hair hung down her back and was tied with a big, black bow, as was proper for a fourteen-year-old girl. Again she sat up all night in a chair car, not able to sleep as the train swayed and jounced in an even rhythm.

When Ethel arrived in Montreal, she went directly to the theater Mum mum had mentioned in her letter. The box office and lobby were closed. The stage door was blocked by a fat man who seemed ready to split out of his rumpled frock coat. Before Ethel could announce her name, he was pushing her out of the door.

"This is rehearsal time. No one gets in," he said gruffly.

"But I've come to see my grandmother, Mrs. Drew."

"Why didn't you say so?" He opened the door reluctantly and jabbed a thumb over his shoulder in the direction of the stage. Ethel made her way between coils of rope that manipulated the furled backdrops. Sandbags, counterbalancing the weight of suspended scenery, leaned against each other like bored spectators. The stage floor was streaked with dirt and here and there starred with chalk marks. Uncle Sidney and Aunt Gladys were reading their lines to an empty chair between them. Their voices echoed through the vast emptiness of the theater. Mrs. Drew was sitting in front of the darkened footlights on a stool that she occupied as if it were a throne. She nodded her head to Ethel in the wings and continued to listen to the actors on the stage. When a natural break did come in the scene, she beckoned Ethel toward her.

"We expected you two days ago" were her words of greeting.

Ethel stammered something about having to make train connections, but her grandmother interrupted. "No matter. You are to be Julia. I hope you are a fast learner." She handed Ethel a stack of papers curling at the corners, on which the dialogue and cues for the first act were handwritten. "Go to your dressing room and start reading."

Ethel had planned to ask for some money for food. She had eaten nothing since she had left school, having had to pay more for her train ticket than she had expected. It was mid-afternoon now, so she guessed she could wait until the cast took their break for supper.

Ethel left the stage in search of the dressing room. The stage-door guardian pointed to a single door at the right. The dressing room was bare except for a table with a row of jars and pots for makeup and a horizontal pole on which the costumes hung. A gas lamp glowed softly in a bracket on the wall. By standing directly under its small circle of light, Ethel could read the script. She was surprised that there were so many lines for Julia. She had expected her first part to be a "walk-on," with little to try her talent. She was pleased but worried. Julia made her entrance almost at the beginning of the first act. Ethel read the lines over to herself, then out loud. She was on the third reading when Mum mum entered. Mrs. Drew swept across the tiny room and hugged her granddaughter, her former businesslike abruptness melting in a warm smile.

"I'm glad you're here, dear. You should be with the family. No better way to learn than from the Drews. Julia will be just right for you." Mrs. Drew stood back a step or two, then said, "You look more like your mother every day."

She could have said nothing more wonderful to Ethel. Her hunger and loneliness and fear were forgotten. Then the far-away look in Mrs. Drew's eyes focused on the script. "You can study that tonight while the rest of us are at the theater. Tomorrow morning we will pick out your costume, and by tomorrow night you should be ready."

"Oh, but I couldn't. When will I have a chance to re-hearse?" asked Ethel in disbelief. She was sure she would never be able to memorize the lines in this scene alone. And then who would show her, tell her, how to act?

"The rest of the players know the lines. You need only fit yours with theirs," said Mrs. Drew.

That was the only instruction ever given Ethel by any of her family during her career. She was just supposed to *know* how to act.

The next twenty-four hours were a nightmare for Ethel. She read the script over and over. She thought she knew her lines, but where was she to stand? When should she be seated? At which side of the stage should she make her exit? No one had bothered to give her a script with stage direc-tions.

Ethel left her room three hours before curtain time. She had only a few short blocks to walk from the hotel to the theater, but she wanted to be sure she'd be there in time. A sharp wind whipped snow in her face. A passing carriage threw slush against her ankles. Her teeth began to chatter, her body to tremble. What if she lost her voice on stage? She felt herself sinking into a dizzy whirl of nausea. Would she ever be able to live through her first performance?

Maybe the weather would keep the audience at home. Maybe there would be no play tonight. Her shoulders relaxed for a moment until she remembered what Mum mum had said long ago: "I have never canceled a scheduled performance and never intend to." It was not the cold that brought on another spate of trembling.

Ethel's steps slowed as she came to the impressive marquee of the theater. A witch-faced woman squatted on a nail keg, selling roasted chestnuts. Teakettle steam escaped from her cauldron. Its shifting current of welcome warmth swept past Ethel's face. The playbill frame next to the darkened ticket window announced that Mrs. John Drew and an all-star cast were appearing in Sheridan's *The Rivals*.

"All-star"? It was true. In one production or another, every performer had had the chance to play a lead; Mr. Jefferson, the producer, had gathered together a prodigious billing of talent. Only because of Mrs. Drew's urging had he revived the part of Julia, which was often omitted from the play, to give Ethel a role for her stage debut. Wouldn't her own nervous clumsiness on stage be noticed all the more because of the professional performances of the rest of the cast?

If Ethel disgraced the family, maybe she could return to school and study music. But how would she support herself? The answer always came back to the stage. She must succeed.

Ethel hugged her mother's worn, but elegantly embossed, black velvet cape around her shoulders and darted past the bolted doors of the theater lobby to the stage entrance in the alley. A blizzard of dirty papers swirled over her head. She strained to open the stage door against the wind. Big Bobby, the man who checked to make sure that only the "right people" entered this exclusively private part of the theater, dozed in a rickety chair. He shook himself out of his sleep and looked at the wall clock with surprise. "You're early, real early," he said to her.

Ethel nodded and hurried past him to the dressing room she would share with all the rest of the women except Mum mum, who, after so many years of performances, had earned a room to herself. Only one light had been lit, an oil lamp on the table by the mirror. A sooty odor hung in the air. The room was cold, for the warmth of the outer theater rarely mixed with the stale dampness of the backstage rooms. She had two hours to wait. Ethel looked around her and saw the rows of jars in front of the mirror. She had watched her mother and grandmother many times as they applied the rouge and powder that gave them a petal-pink glow across the footlights. She opened the first of the jars and timidly applied a layer of cream. Then, dipping her finger into the rose paste, she dabbed two spots of color on her cheeks, a bit of red on her lips, and dusted all with a cloud of powder. She squinted at herself in the mirror. She felt she had successfully hidden her fourteen-year-old schoolgirl look. Perhaps she could use a touch more rouge on her cheeks. She did not notice that someone had entered the shadowy room.

"And what do you think you are doing?" It was Mum mum's voice in an annoyed mood.

Ethel turned quickly. "I'm just putting on my makeup."

"Scrub it off."

"I thought . . ." Ethel hesitated. "You . . ."

"I use it because I am an old woman and wish to hide the fact. You, Ethel, have no need for it." Her grandmother's voice softened. "I thought you might be here early. This is a lonely place, but you can use your time to better advantage going over your lines."

"I'm sure I know them," said Ethel.

"So am I, but I read them over before every performance to set the scene in my mind. I'll be in my dressing room if you need me," said Mum mum.

Ethel turned back to the mirror. Her cheeks burned under their pink and white mask. She took a clean towel from the washstand and rubbed the makeup off as best she could. Her own coloring flamed up on her cheeks. She turned to the dialogue she had so carefully memorized, noting especially the heavily underlined cue markings indicating where she was to make her entrances.

An hour later, Aunt Gladys Rankin, Uncle Sidney's wife, arrived with the other two members of the female cast. They chatted gaily and asked Ethel a dozen questions. "What was the weather like in Philadelphia? Was your train on time?" Ethel knew they were trying to make her feel at ease, but it didn't help.

It was time to hook herself into her elaborately ruffled costume. She had been advanced the only money she was to earn for the run of the play to buy the gown. Ethel had chosen blue, remembering that it had been her mother's favorite color. After she slipped into the beautiful dress, she was afraid to sit down for fear of rumpling it. Her heart was pounding noisily in her ears. She gulped air to breathe. How could actors endure such torture? Or was she the only one who felt this fear?

Aunt Gladys handed her a handkerchief. "Take this, Ethel," she said. "It will give you something to do with your hands, and besides, it helps to keep them dry."

Ethel noticed that Aunt Gladys was dabbing at her own palms. The prompter knocked on the door. "Five minutes, ladies." Their chatter abruptly stopped. Ethel could hear someone playing a piano from the orchestra pit. She wished desperately that she could change places with the musician. The creak of pulleys and a smattering of applause told the actresses that the curtain had been raised. Aunt Gladys blew out the light in the dressing room and opened the door to the darkened wings of the stage. Two male servants in the play, Thomas and Fag, had the opening lines. As soon as they made their exits, Lydia, played by Aunt Gladys, and Lucy, played by Gladys's mother, arrived on the scene and seated themselves on a sofa. A page of script later, Julia, whom Ethel played, was to make her entrance.

Ethel stood in the wings in a state of shock. She had to remember to sweep in gracefully from the right, embrace Lydia without turning her back to the audience, without stumbling over the table in front of her, without forgetting her next speech.

There was her cue: "Lud, Ma'am, here is Miss Melville."

Ethel hurried onto the stage. Suddenly she was blinded by the footlights, but she found her place and heard herself whisper, "Lydia, our pleasure is the greater." She must speak up next time.

She seated herself on the sofa near Lydia and waited for her aunt's next line. Something was wrong. Aunt Gladys's eyes had a glazed, puzzled look; she was fumbling with her handkerchief in her lap. Her lips whispered the words, "Keep going, Ethel."

Ethel suddenly realized that it was her aunt who had forgotten the script. She was used to playing the role without the part of Julia. Ethel began her next speech, a question that she at once answered briskly with Aunt Gladys's response. For the next two minutes Ethel kept up a running patter of dialogue until Aunt Gladys's memory returned and she could take over as planned.

The next character to make her entrance was Mum mum herself, as Mrs. Malaprop, her plump figure laced into a majestic wall of black lace, her white wig towering pompously, her feathered fan fluttering dramatically. She swept onto the stage amid applause and crossed to Ethel's side. Turning her face ever so slightly away from the audience, she smiled and whispered, "Good."

From that moment on Ethel began to relax. She played her part well, even enjoying herself. When the final curtain fell, she knew she had nothing to be ashamed of. She had proudly joined the family ranks of professional actors. When she returned to the dressing room, a large, red apple was waiting for her. Aunt Gladys hugged her hard, and Mum mum smiled proudly. Ethel knew what the apple meant. Although no one seemed to remember when the tradition had started, when any member of the Drew family had an important first night, an apple was the acknowledgment of a job well done. This was the first of many red apples Ethel was to receive.

7

Ethel had hardly broken into her role when Grandmother Drew left the company to tend to some family business in New York. Mrs. Rankin, Aunt Gladys's mother, moved up to the starring role of Mrs. Malaprop. She spoke her lines well, with just the right touch of haughty confusion, but she did not draw the audience that Mrs. Drew had brought to the theater. Uncle Sidney, who had been left as manager of the troupe, could no longer count on a full house to pay the bills.

Every evening as the piano player pounded out his uninspired mood music and the pulley creaked to raise the curtain, Ethel listened to the applause and tried to guess how many people there were out front. It was more than just a game. It gave the answer as to whether they'd gather for their delightful midnight suppers. Most often Uncle Sidney would shake his head and say, "Two meals are quite enough if we are all to keep in shape."

Ethel did not wholly agree, as she was awake in the morning hours before the others, a habit she could not break from convent days. It wasn't that anyone ever went hungry, but it was obvious that expenses had to be cut somewhere. The cast was no longer housed in modest hotels but in more modest boardinghouses.

Ethel spent much of her time walking the streets of strange cities rather than returning to her depressingly cramped quarters, which frequently were in someone's converted attic. Being the youngest member of the cast, she drew the least desirable accommodations.

Sometimes when Ethel arrived at the theater early, she would tiptoe across the stage as prop men hauled the furniture around to match the chalk marks on the floor. Cautiously she would peek through a slit in the curtain to watch the audience file into the theater. Often it frightened her to look at the faces she was to entertain, the old man complaining about his gout, the young woman telling her companion she'd rather be seeing a tragedy. It was better to think of people on the other side of the footlights as a faceless crowd.

But as the crowd dwindled, so did the actors' fortune. The final humiliation came one Saturday night in Saint John, New Brunswick. The theater was quite empty, and Ethel noticed that Uncle Sidney was speaking his lines so fast that it was hard for anyone to keep up the breathless pace. The moment the curtain fell, he assembled the cast and gave them instructions to go directly to the station. The train would be waiting.

"But I'll have to go back to my room to get my suitcase," Ethel said.

"That will be taken care of," Uncle Sidney answered impatiently.

Ethel questioned no one further and hurried to the dressing room to get her cape and nothing else. Aunt Gladys was the last to leave the stage door, but she finally caught up with

Ethel. Ethel noticed she was strangely silent and strangely plump. Aunt Gladys was always very careful about keeping her hair the same shade of burnished copper and her waistline the same unbelievable measurement that could be spanned by her dainty hands. Tonight she had ballooned to buxom proportions that not even her coat could hide. Only after they had boarded the train and left Saint John behind did Ethel guess the secret of the change. Aunt Gladys discreetly retired to the rest room in the coach car and returned in a few minutes carrying five dresses, which she tried to tie in a bundle and wrap in a petticoat.

"I wasn't going to leave these behind for that horrible woman who refused even to furnish a pillow for my bed," said Aunt Gladys.

"What do you mean?" asked Ethel.

"Didn't Sidney tell you? Oh, I guess not. He wouldn't want to discourage you so soon. It just happens, Ethel, that our funds came to an end before we could quite balance them against our room and theater rent. If we had returned we might have been greeted by a constable."

"But my clothes, everything I own, are back there in my trunk," cried Ethel.

"Hush, dear, don't think about it," said Aunt Gladys. "We'll get around to paying our accounts. Drews always do, and they'll save it for you, I know."

Years later Ethel's little trunk was returned to her, but by then her dresses were quite out of style.

The company's return to New York was far from triumphant, but Ethel was glad to see Mum mum again. Mrs. Drew had always been able to solve the family problems in the past. Now suddenly even her magic seemed powerless; the mysterious business she had rushed to New York to handle had not developed an income. The theaters in New York and Philadelphia were booked with other companies. Mrs. Drew could not even find backers for a western road tour. Fortunately, at that time of crisis, her son, John Drew, who had been extremely successful on the London stage, returned to New York and solved the immediate financial problem.

But Mrs. Drew was not used to being dependent upon others. It irritated her; it infuriated her. It was beyond understanding why any Drew, especially herself, should not be able to demand top billing and salary on any stage. Her age had something to do with the situation, but the rest of the family's fortunes were affected also by the formation of a theatrical syndicate that was organizing traveling companies for the entire country. For Ethel, a fifteen-year-old girl who had appeared on the stage in one role, the future looked black.

John Drew — they all called him Uncle Jack — provided Ethel with a small room next to Mum mum's in the Sherman Square Hotel. It was just large enough for one bed, which sagged in the middle like a lumpy hammock, and one table with a splinted leg. Ethel tacked up a picture of her favorite actor, William Gillette, on one wall and a reproduction of a painting entitled "Spring Garden," adding color and camouflage to another bit of cracked plaster. These were the only adornments she could afford.

When her brother John first came from school to see her, he immediately dubbed her quarters the "friar's cell," but he continued to return on many forbidden weekends of freedom and always declared the cell was heaven compared to academic seclusion.

Ethel would gladly have traded places with him. Her time was rarely free. In the mornings she boarded a five-cent horsecar near the hotel and got off at Broadway in the heart of the theatrical district. On days when even the nickel was an extravagance, she walked the blocks, arriving tired and exhausted before her search for a job even began.

First she'd try the offices of Fernandez, Simons, and Brown. According to Grandmother Drew, there was a certain amount of prestige to be gained if she could get a listing through their contacts. The offices were far from impressive. One hard, backless bench was lined up opposite the door to the inner office, into which only the chosen few passed. The walls were painted a shade of putty that faded in streaks of umber near the window. Ethel had spent so many hours staring at the wall that she was beginning to see forms and faces in the mottled colors.

Exercising her imagination in this way helped her to pass the hours she spent sitting beside other hopeful young actors and actresses "at liberty." At times, one or another of them would speak, mentioning the time, the weather, the opening of a new play, but never would their pride let them admit how desperate they really were. Instead they all hid their problems with depressing, make-believe optimism. There was always a great part that had been promised and would soon materialize, a rehearsal that had temporarily been postponed. It sickened Ethel to hear the actors lie to one another, yet it was surely better than if they had complained and begged for deserved sympathy. Ethel rarely spoke, waiting silently every day to hear the same words, "Nothing now."

Ethel had a regular routine, having worked out the closest routes between offices so that she wouldn't waste time between calls. Often she received the discouraging word so fast that she had time left over at the end of the day, but she was ashamed to come home any sooner than usual, afraid that Mum mum or Uncle Jack would feel she hadn't really tried.

Mum mum would not hear of Ethel's applying for any

sort of work outside the theater. "Of course you will find a proper role," she repeated. Mrs. Drew had always had a commanding manner. Even now she refused to be discouraged. Instead of letting her shoulders droop, she made her back straighter and straighter; her brows furrowed in determination that could not help but be transferred to others. So each morning Ethel would carefully brush her hair, pinch her cheeks to substitute for the forbidden rouge, smooth the creases out of her one good serge suit, and head in search of that elusive stage role.

In the meantime, Uncle Jack was proving Mrs. Drew's confidence that employment was available, and for Uncle Jack, employment included starring roles. John Drew was a dashing man with an elegant moustache; he could successfully play the romantic gentleman in the popular drawing-room comedies of the day. He acted his role as conscientiously off stage as on but never vied for the dramatic attention his brother-in-law, Maurice Barrymore, demanded. He was liked by everyone.

The producer Charles Frohman had been the first to capitalize on John Drew's popularity. Frohman could see the box office advantage of building a star. For him the play was not as important as the player, and the public proved him right.

Charles Frohman was a short, tubby man with a round face and turned-up mouth punctuated almost constantly with the stub of a cigar. He was genial and patient, able to cope with the temperaments of those whose names he put in lights above theater marquees. Uncle Jack was not the only member of the family Frohman had booked. He had given parts to Georgie and Maurice Barrymore in some of his touring companies when he himself was a very young man just making the change from press agent to producer.

Perhaps because of a bit of sentiment, and more probably because of the thought that the Barrymore name might someday be revived in public memory, Frohman was persuaded by Uncle Jack to give Ethel a tea-carrying job on stage in a play called *The Bauble Shop*. The stars included Uncle Jack, Maude Adams, and Elsie De Wolf. Having been surrounded almost all her life by famous names of the theater, Ethel was unimpressed, although she was delighted suddenly to become financially independent and to put behind her the days of waiting in agents' offices. To justify the handsome salary of thirty dollars a week that he offered Ethel, Frohman stipulated that she understudy the part played by Miss De Wolf. Ethel obediently memorized the entire play, which she seemed to be able to do with far greater ease than the rest of the cast, but Miss De Wolf never once missed a performance. Ethel remained in her pert little maid's uniform.

When the three-month run in New York was completed, the play was scheduled for a cross-country tour. Ethel was sure that her part would be eliminated altogether for the out-of-town performances. Each day she waited with dread to see if such a notice would be posted on the backstage bulletin board. The board stayed blank, but an interesting rumor filtered through the cast that Elsie De Wolf had decided to stay in New York when the play went on the road, which left the part of Lady Kate Fennell open.

Before Ethel's courage could leave her, she went straight to Charles Frohman's office. It was not far from the putty-hued premises of Fernandez, Simons, and Brown, but the location was the only similarity. A turkey-red carpet covered the floor of Frohman's outer office. The handsome wall paneling was almost completely covered with photographs of some of Broadway's greatest stars, all attesting their affection and gratitude in handwritten flourishes across their portraits. An impeccably dressed young man presided over the desk that guarded the door to Frohman's inner office. For some strange reason, no one was waiting to see Mr. Frohman, which gave Ethel heart, but the young man undermined her confidence with his question, "And do you have an appointment, Miss?"

"No, but just tell Mr. Frohman that Miss Barrymore is here."

It was the first time that Ethel had ever used her name as a passport for entry, but now she spoke the word with just the right touch of imperious dignity to send the young secretary on his way with the message.

Suddenly Ethel realized what a preposterous suggestion she was about to make to the great Mr. Frohman — that is, if the impresario would even grant her an audience. Any one of half a dozen framed faces on the wall would gladly accept the part if it were offered. Ethel decided to leave at once, before she had to face the humiliating scene of being fired from the cast completely.

At that moment the door opened again, and Charles Frohman was standing in front of her. He greeted her with the same deference he might have used for Mrs. Drew herself, which made Ethel even more nervous than before. He pulled out a chair for her to be seated and returned to his throne behind a massive desk.

For an agonizing moment, Ethel couldn't find her voice. Then in one rush the words tumbled out. "I'd like to play the part of Lady Fennell."

Frohman grinned good-naturedly. "How old are you, young lady?" he asked.

"Fifteen," Ethel answered.

"And do you know that the program lists the part of Lady Fennell as a fashionable woman of the world of thirty-two?" he continued.

"I can make myself look older, Mr. Frohman, and I just know I can act the part. I've memorized the lines, and you'd never be able to break in someone else so soon," Ethel said.

Frohman settled back in his chair, rolled his cigar between two fingers thoughtfully, and made the pronouncement, "Try it at the Wednesday matinee."

Ethel floated back to the theater in a haze of excitement. She was afraid to tell Uncle Jack what she had done. If she ruined her part, she would ruin the whole play. She'd been a fool to think she could do it, but now her chin went up and her shoulders straightened. Mum mum never would have given up.

The next day Ethel took some of the money she had saved and went straight to a theatrical costumer. She rented a flaming red wig and a daring black gown beaded in swirls of jet. She stood in front of the mirror, surveying the transformation with satisfaction.

On Wednesday, when Uncle Jack heard the news of the casting change, he rushed to Ethel's dressing room. When she greeted him, he hardly recognized his niece. After faltering for a moment, he took her hand. "Ethel, by jove, you've done it. You are Lady Kate. Of course you've aged me a full generation in one day," he said.

Ethel smiled nervously. She felt far from the poised character she was to portray. The rest of the cast congratulated her and wished her luck, all except Miss De Wolf, who refused to let Ethel borrow any of the gorgeous costumes made especially for her by the French designer Paquin. Miss De

Wolf even threatened a lawsuit if Frohman distributed the play programs that afternoon with her name still listed as playing Lady Fennell.

Frohman managed to calm Miss De Wolf, but no one could have calmed Ethel's terror as she waited in the wings for her cue. Her face flushed to a color almost matching her wig. Her mouth was dry. She held her breath and counted to twenty. Nothing seemed to slow her racing pulse, but as she stepped in front of the footlights with her head raised high, all outward signs of palpitation left her. What the audience saw was a tall young woman with a willowy figure, radiant complexion, and sea-green eyes. Her voice was deep and rolled in waves of sound. This was not the timid little girl whose mother had told her, "Look up, Pauline," but a handsome woman of the world of thirty-two. Ethel had earned a second red apple.

Frohman gave the nod, and Ethel was signed to play the part of Lady Fennell on tour.

8

The tour took the acting company to the cities of Boston, Philadelphia, Chicago, and St. Louis. One newspaper critic wrote: "An opalescent dream named Ethel Barrymore came on and played Lady Kate."

Ethel had never heard the word *opalescent*. Nervously she clipped the piece and showed it to her Uncle Jack. "Does it mean I ruined the performance?" she asked.

John Drew read the clipping and doubled up with laughter. "It's the first time I've heard of an actress who can't recognize a compliment when she sees one. Go to the dictionary, young lady. That's a word you should never forget."

There were others who were discovering this "opalescent dream." Many of Uncle Jack's friends stopped by for visits. Dates without a chaperon were unheard of in those days, and of course Ethel's evenings were never free, but she delighted in the visitors' company during teatime. Richard Harding Davis was one of her favorites. Dick, as Ethel called him, was a young man of wealth and social standing, but at the time all that mattered was that he could talk to Ethel about London. Since the age of six, she had wanted to return to England, for it was a country with a queen and maybe even fairy princesses, if she wished hard enough. Ethel had reached that puzzling time of life in which one day she was still a young child with dreams of castles in the sky, and the next, a mature young adult lunching with her Uncle Jack at the British Embassy in Washington.

For the first time in her life, Ethel was being treated as a fashionable young lady. In Baltimore she was invited to the swank Hunt Ball. In Chicago she met the Medill McCormicks and the Fields; in Cincinnati she became acquainted with the prominent Longworths. A society reporter commented in 1896 that "her manners are unaffected and she has a frank unconventionality which is refreshing without being bizarre."

Ethel never completely lost her shyness, but she found that when she behaved naturally, like the young actress in training she was, people appreciated her unexpected modesty. Actresses were apt not to confine their acting to the stage, but Ethel's youthful naiveté added to her charm.

Her special schoolgirl crush was William Gillette, whose portrait had decorated her "friar's cell." Luckily Gillette held his matinees on Thursdays instead of the usual Wednesdays, and so Ethel could be in his audience every week. Uncle Jack had arranged for a free admission pass and finally was even able to arrange for their meeting at luncheon one day.

Ethel sat tongue-tied, a role Gillette much appreciated, for he relished the idea of entertaining a charming, attractive young listener. He was now forty-two years old and had been playing leads in all the fashionable plays of the day for the past twenty years; he was still aloofly handsome, with a craggy profile and what had been termed "smoldering" eyes. He had attended college at both Yale and Harvard, which was unusual for a member of the theatrical profession, and Gillette emphasized the fact frequently. He could and would discuss almost any subject as if he were an authority. To many he was an insufferable bore, but to Ethel he was a brilliant, mature hero.

A month after the luncheon, Ethel received a telegram from Charles Frohman: "Would you like to go to London with Gillette in *Secret Service?*" At first she was afraid someone was playing a joke, but Uncle Jack confirmed the unbelievable news. She was so excited she almost forgot to answer the wire. Two dreams were coming true at once. She would be appearing on the stage with William Gillette himself, and she would be visiting her fairy kingdom of castles and queens.

Everyone in the family must know. She rushed to tell Mum mum, who was quietly pleased. Then Ethel sent a wire to her father, whom she had not seen in months, although he was staying at the Lambs Club, headquarters for actors in the city. Maurice sent word that he was delighted with her success and would give her letters of introduction to his friends in London. He would be at the dock to see her off. He never appeared, but Ethel was so excited about her trip that the disappointment was easily ignored.

Her own luggage had been stowed in her cabin hours before sailing. Ethel stood at the ship's rail watching the buildings of New York fade above a watery horizon. Harry Woodruff, another actor in the company, was standing with her when Gillette strolled by. When the star saw young Ethel, he smiled and took her hand in his, squeezing it just a bit as he bowed to kiss her glove. Suddenly, for no apparent reason at all except that he had held her hand for a second too long, Ethel's heroic picture of Gillette shattered. In daylight, without the safe distance of the footlights between them, Gillette returned to mere mortal status, and for the entire run of the play, Ethel responded coldly to the puzzled politeness of the star who had made her trip to magical London possible.

Getting off the train in Waterloo station in London, Ethel felt strangely at home. Perhaps it was the smell of wet rain on the wooden pavement that brought back childhood memories.

Ethel's part in *Secret Service* was very small, although she had been engaged to understudy the ingenue role played by Odette Taylor. Ethel had seen the play in New York so many times that she already knew most of the lines by heart. She was the only new member of the cast; few rehearsals were scheduled, and she had hours of free time to revisit the historical sites and museums of the city. She was having a delightful time without having to work at all.

The summer of 1897 was a time of excitement in London, the summer of Queen Victoria's diamond jubilee, celebrating the sixty years of her reign. There were parades, such as the magnificent spectacle of Indian princes garbed in jewels from chin to waist, that far surpassed Ethel's make-believe dreams or any theatrical spectacle attempted on stage. Ethel didn't miss a moment as a spectator on the edge of the crowds. Many Americans had taken the opportunity to be in England during the celebrations, and some were friends of the Drew family. Ethel had no chance to feel alone in a strange country.

Many of her father's friends also called, and suddenly the doors to some of the greatest homes of England were opened to her. Without quite realizing how special these opportunities were, Ethel met the Duchess of Sutherland, Bernard Shaw, Lawrence Irving, Lady Lister-Kaye, and Prince Francis of Teck, whom they all called Frankie Teck and whose sister was the Duchess of York. England was the place for Ethel. She had fallen in love with the country, and the sentiment seemed to be mutual.

The play that had brought her to London continued to be a success. Ethel's pleasant routine seemed unlikely to be broken until one night Odette Taylor fainted just before making her entrance. Ethel was sitting on stage in her nurse's costume. The curtain was hastily lowered, and Ethel was told to take over the lead. Panic-stricken, she cried, "But I can't. I've never played it before. I've only read the lines."

There was no arguing. She had been hired as an understudy, and she had to go on. Quickly she rushed upstairs to Miss Taylor's dressing room, unfastening the apron of her nurse's uniform as she went. When she reached the star's room, Ethel suddenly realized that Miss Taylor had been rushed to the hospital in her costume. Ethel would have to go on stage with what she was wearing. There was no time for her to go over her lines, no time to do anything but stumble on stage for her cue.

Someone had already made the announcement that Miss Ethel Barrymore was taking over the part for the evening. Polite applause welcomed her entrance. Ethel played the first scene completely in a daze. During the next act, the lines she was mouthing began to take on meaning, and she consciously tried to mimic the actions and directions she knew Miss Taylor had been given.

When the curtain finally came down at the end of the play, the audience thundered their approval. She wasn't sure whether the applause was for her performance or for her pluckiness at having filled in at the last moment. Her doubts were soon put to rest. Odette Taylor was forced to cancel the rest of her engagement with the company; Ethel was provided with a proper costume, and for the next two weeks she continued to play the lead. Word had gotten around that in her first performance she had been charming. Some London critics came to see her and praised her in print. Ethel was sure that this was the break that would bring her stardom in her own right. When rumors reached her that another actress had been sent for to take over the role, she wouldn't believe it — not after the reviews. But it was true. Brokenhearted, Ethel returned to her small part as the nurse.

For days she hid her gloom in the privacy of her room on Chapel Street. Not until a month later, when Ben Webster, an important actor, and his wife, May Whitty, insisted that she come to a party at their home, did Ethel see any of her friends again. That evening she met the Duke of York, who would later become king of England. He asked her, "Aren't you the little girl I saw in *Secret Service?*"

She stammered, "Yes," not quite believing she would be recognized by anyone as important as he.

"I liked your performance so much I returned to see it a second time," the duke continued. "I was disappointed to see that someone else had taken over the role. She was not nearly as good as you, Miss Barrymore."

Ethel's face flushed with pleasure. The duke's compliment almost made up for the disappointment of having to play the part of the nurse each night.

With so many flattering opinions of her talent, Ethel decided that when *Secret Service* closed and the cast returned home, she would remain in England. She was sure that she could find some work on the London stage. But it was not that easy. Again she plodded from one office or theater to another, carrying with her the encouraging reviews that had been printed in the London papers, but other actresses with equally brilliant references joined her in the waiting lines.

Ethel's friends had no idea how strained her finances had become. Her small savings paid for her lodgings, but there was little left for food. She lived a strange life, floating between the world of high society and the poverty of unemployment. She discovered that, when not asked to some lavish dinner party, she could satisfy her hunger for a whole day with just a meal of dates. She had one black dress and one white one that she kept changing by adding or subtracting a bit of trimming.

To her surprise, Ethel found that the British were not half as snobbish as the Americans. Titles did not seem to matter as much as whether people liked you or not, and Ethel was adored by almost everyone she met. However, she realized she could not live on the hospitality of her friends forever. When she received word from Uncle Jack that he would be in London for a few days, she rushed to see him.

"I can't find work, Uncle Jack. I've tried, but for every part there are a dozen people asking. Will you take me home with you?" she asked.

John Drew answered with surprise. "Of course, Ethel, but I thought you were the toast of London."

"If I'd been all that good, I wouldn't still be looking for a part," she said.

"I guess you're right, but it takes an honest person to admit it." He looked at her forlorn face. "Come on, cheer up. You're going to dinner with me tonight. It's a farewell party in my honor. We'll share the stage."

Ethel looked up at his smile. It was good to have uncles like Uncle Jack.

She thanked him and returned to her room to pack. There wasn't very much to put in her trunk She couldn't fold away the memories of her six glorious months in London, but she'd have them with her always. Oh, why did she have to go back? She threw herself on the bed in tears. She was being foolish, she knew. She was acting her real age, not the age of the mature young woman she had been trying to play these past weeks. She buried her head in the pillow. When her sobs stopped, she had fallen asleep.

Two hours later she was wakened by a knock on her door. The driver of a hansom cab was standing in the hall with a written message. It said: "Dear little Bullfinch [a nickname only Ellen Terry ever used], I hear you're going back to America. Come down to the theater tonight to say goodbye to Sir Henry and me. Ellen."

Ethel had met the famous actress and her distinguished husband only a few times. How wonderful it was to be remembered by so many.

Ethel washed her face and bathed her eyes. She wrote a note for her Uncle Jack saying that she would meet him later at the Savoy. Then, dressing carefully for the supper party that was to close the evening, she walked to the theater to say goodbye to her friends.

Ellen Terry rushed to embrace Ethel. "So you're going back to America," she said. "Tell me all the things you've been doing here in London, Ethel."

Ethel told her about a weekend she had spent with the Sutherlands and about a party with Lord and Lady Lewis, whose daughter Elsie was just Ethel's age. She talked on and on.

Ellen Terry said, "America is such a long distance away. When will we see you again?"

Ethel shook her head.

"Well, we'll see about that. Run along and say goodbye to Sir Henry. He wants to see you, too."

Ethel knocked timidly on Sir Henry's door. She was answered by a gruff, "Come in." Sir Henry Irving's sideburns brushed bushily from the sides of his face. His kindness was masked by an austere profile and commanding manner. "So you want to go back to America?"

"Oh, no, Sir Henry," Ethel answered. "I don't, but I can't find any work."

"And how would you like to stay here and join our cast? There are always parts for fresh young talent."

"Oh, Sir Henry!" Ethel couldn't think of a thing to say. Tears filled her eyes for the second time that day.

Sir Henry went on. "You could play Annette in *The Bells*, and there's a part in my son Lawrence's play. Heavens, with that emotion we should cast you in a tragedy."

Ethel tried to smile, but her voice still caught in her throat. "Oh, thank you," she said.

"You can sign the contract now," Sir Henry said. "Rehearsals won't start until summer, but I'll send you the script to study. Now be off. Your youth depresses me when I know it will take at least an hour at the paint pots for me to imitate what I have long since lost."

Ethel walked out the door and stumbled over some props in the dark. She didn't feel a thing, hardly saw a thing. She was thinking only of the fabulous good turn in her fortunes. Outside the theater she wanted to run and sing and shout. She noticed people staring at her and realized that she had been smiling at the world. Such a wonderful world!

Ethel hailed a cab to take her to the Savoy for the supper party. When she entered, she saw Uncle Jack surrounded by friends, many of the most important people of the British theater. She was late. They were about to be seated. Ethel was placed across the table from Mrs. Patrick Campbell, who had been a close friend of her mother.

The conversation spun around her head: what new plays were opening, who was to play the lead in what production. She was deciding how to make her own exciting announcement when Mrs. Campbell turned to her and said, "We're so sorry, dear, that you will be leaving us."

"Oh, but I'm not," said Ethel.

Uncle Jack's soup spoon stopped in mid-air. Everybody at the table started to ask questions.

"I've just signed a contract to appear with Sir Henry Irving and Ellen Terry," Ethel announced.

Uncle Jack stood up and spoke gruffly. "Well, this family certainly knows how to keep secrets from each other." Then, smiling proudly, he continued, "But I am delighted, Ethel. You will be in excellent company and should learn a thing or two."

Another guest rose. "I propose a toast to a new star of the stage, to Ethel Barrymore." Congratulations were offered on every side, and the party turned into a happy celebration for Ethel instead of a farewell for John Drew.

9

It was still two months before rehearsals for *The Bells* would be called. Ethel had received a letter from her brother John saying that Mum mum's health was failing. Quite suddenly Ethel decided that she must return to America to see her grandmother. She'd always felt very close to Mum mum. It was true that Mrs. Drew was strict; she would not tolerate laziness or laxness toward duty, but she handed out love as lavishly as discipline. She was the one who had come to the convent recitals, and the one who had tucked a frilly handkerchief or bottle of fragrance in with Ethel's uniforms. It didn't seem possible that anyone as ageless as Mrs. Drew could reach a time of infirmity. Ethel knew she wouldn't be able to leave England once the play opened, so she borrowed money from a friend and booked passage on the next ship home.

Her grandmother was staying in a small hotel in Larchmont. A wide veranda ran around three sides of the old building. A group of elderly ladies were knitting on one side of the porch. Ethel smiled when she saw that Mum mum had engaged a handsome old gentleman with white hair and a clipped beard in a game of chess. Mrs. Drew chuckled as she made the next successful move.

Ethel waited a moment before greeting her grandmother. It was a shock to see that the plump figure had slimmed so drastically, that the Drew nose now so dominated a thinning face. Only the artful application of powder and rouge kept Mum mum's face from matching the blotched yellow coloring of her hands.

"Mum mum . . ." Ethel began.

"Why, Ethel, what on earth are you doing here?"

Ethel laughed at her surprise. The chess board was put away, and the handsome gentleman excused himself so they could visit.

"Jack tells me you've entranced the lords of England. Now what about your stage career?" Mrs. Drew asked.

Ethel told her of the exciting chance to play with Sir Henry Irving and Ellen Terry.

Mum mum nodded. "Watch them and you'll learn."

"Where is the rest of the family?" Ethel asked.

"Here and there," Mrs. Drew said. "Jack is playing in *Rosemary* in Salt Lake City. Sidney is in Australia. Lionel's in some road company, can't remember where, and your brother John humors an old lady by dropping in to see me every day. He thinks he's an artist now."

They talked until the knitting needles were put away and the other guests started for the dining room.

"They feed us gruel here, or I'd invite you to stay," Mum mum said.

"No, I must go," said Ethel, "but I'll be back tomorrow."

For the next two weeks, Ethel and John took turns entertaining Mrs. Drew, though she more frequently ended by entertaining them. Ethel was so sure that Mum mum was as spry as anyone her age could hope to be that she was especially shocked to receive a cable, a week after she returned to England, saying that her grandmother had died in her sleep. One hour later the postman brought a letter from Mrs. Drew, written the day she died, thanking Ethel for having taken the time to visit her.

Tears wouldn't come. Ethel sat in her room looking at the familiar handwriting. There was so much about Mum mum to remember: her performances on stage, her words of encouragement in New York. It didn't seem possible that it was all over.

Suddenly Ethel looked at her watch. She was late for her first rehearsal. When she arrived at the theater, Sir Henry was pacing the stage. The rest of the company were standing about nervously.

"You are tardy, Miss Barrymore," he said coldly.

"I know, Sir Henry. I just received word that my grandmother has died."

His scowl faded. "Mrs. John Drew?"

Ethel nodded.

"Go home, my dear," Sir Henry said. "No rehearsal for you today."

Although Ethel had a large part in the play to memorize, the role did not tax her dramatic ability. She had only to look pretty and smile a lot. But life was exciting and fun. When the play went on tour in the provinces, she had a chance to enjoy the English countryside. She and Susanne Sheldon, another American girl in the company, shared rooms and laughed at some of the grim places where they had to stay. But frequently the lack of hot water was partly compensated for by the charm of history and old wood.

During the tour they started rehearsal on Lawrence Irving's play called *Peter the Great*. Ethel had always been in awe of Sir Henry Irving. He was a chivalrous man, dedi-

cated to his craft. Now that she was spending much of her
time with his playwright son, Ethel discovered that these
same qualities had been passed on to the next generation.

Lawrence was charming and intense. He had been sent as
a student to Russia, where he had been infected with the
same somberness of mood that characterized the Russian
literature he studied. Lawrence seemed always melancholy
and sad. Ethel at first took it upon herself to cheer him; instead, his gentle sense of tragedy engulfed her. Together they
would share afternoons of complete silence. Sometimes Ethel
played melancholy Russian pieces for him on the piano. They
looked deep into each other's eyes. They fell in love and
became engaged.

Although she hadn't seen her father for several months,
Ethel at once sent a cable to Maurice to announce the news.
Maurice cabled back, "Congratulations. Love, Father."

The moment their engagement was announced, Lawrence
dropped his dark moods of anguish. He became a normal,
happy young man, just like all the other cheerful, hearty
young men whom Ethel met every day. His unique tender
sadness and his need for motherly attention vanished, and
so did Ethel's love.

Ethel was more afraid to tell Sir Henry of her change of
mind than she was of breaking the news to his forever stu-
pidly grinning son, yet both Sir Henry and Lawrence were
understanding. Everyone lived through the temporary crisis,
with only the newspapers making headlines of the event.
Ethel once more went to the cable office, this time to send her
father the news of her broken engagement. Again Maurice
cabled back, "Congratulations. Love, Father."

Ethel was never without a group of admiring escorts.
Very shortly the newspaper headlines announced that Miss

Barrymore had another fiancé. Nothing had been formally announced, but she and Gerald du Maurier were seen everywhere together. Gerald's father, George du Maurier, was the author of *Trilby* and *Peter Ibbetson,* among other literary works. Again Ethel felt that the son had inherited his father's brilliance, but young Gerald was far from impressive in looks. He was frail to the point of emaciation. One reporter commented that "his legs looked for all the world like a couple of sectional gas-pipes with abrupt bony projections midway between the floor and their jointure to the trunk." Ethel insisted to her friends that Gerald's charm and wit more than made up for his lack of a virile physique.

Only Gerald's mother caused Ethel to have doubts. Mrs. du Maurier began to tell Ethel just how to take care of Gerald, what to make him wear in winter, and what to feed him to keep up his strength. Ethel made the sudden decision that she should return to America to think things over. It meant leaving the city she loved and returning to New York, where she had few friends, but she had to go before it was too late.

She had barely enough money to pay for her passage, but she did not hesitate. Her ship, however, landed in Canada unexpectedly, and she had to board the night train for Grand Central Station. She arrived with exactly one quarter in her purse, which she grandly gave to the redcap to carry her bag to a public hansom cab.

"Where to?" the driver asked.

Ethel hesitated. Where to? She didn't know. Then, for no reason at all, except that occasionally Uncle Jack made it his residence, she said, "The Waldorf." She had picked the most expensive hotel in the city.

Rather frightened, she went directly to the registration

desk and was surprised when five young clerks came forward
to greet her with formal ceremony. She was sure she had
been mistaken for someone else, but one of them bowed and
said, "Miss Barrymore, we are so glad to have you with us."

How lovely, how wonderfully lovely to be recognized, but
now she knew she could not go through with the hoax of
registering without any way to pay for the night. She answered timidly, "I just wanted to know if my uncle is here."

"Oh, yes, Mr. Drew is with us. Will you want a room or a
suite?" asked the clerk.

Ethel had never expected such good fortune. Her poise
returned. "I will have a room, and will you please pay for the
cab."

"Of course," the clerk was quick to agree.

Ethel followed the bellboy to her room and collapsed in a
chair. She had a strange, warm feeling that she was returning home. London had been quite unreal. Here she had
been welcomed by her own people in her own country. She
would not forget this comfortable feeling of belonging.

Immediately she called her Uncle Jack's room.

"Who on earth is this?" he exclaimed. "It sounds like
Ethel."

"It is," she laughed.

"But you're in England," he said.

"No, I'm upstairs in the hotel."

"I'll meet you in the dining room in five minutes for
breakfast."

Over coffee and a huge, American-style breakfast — hot
breads and sausages and a heaping plateful of whipped eggs
and fried potatoes — they exchanged news and gossip.

"Your picture has been on the front page of every paper,
young lady," Uncle Jack said. "Having trouble making up

your mind? Not that I objected to your last change of heart."

"Is that why they recognized me in the hotel lobby?"

Of course, it couldn't have been that she'd been recognized as an actress of note. She hadn't proved to have exceptional talent, just a sweet face. Would that be enough to get her a job in New York? After her second cup of coffee, she mentioned the subject.

"I need a job, Uncle Jack. Will you take me to see Mr. Frohman?"

"I see no reason why I should accompany you except to take a lesson or two in how to influence the gentleman. I remember you talked yourself into quite a role before," answered her uncle.

Ethel laughed. She still had the red wig tucked away in the bottom of her trunk.

The next day Charles Frohman greeted them both in his customary jovial manner. "Jack, you have quite a niece here, I see and hear."

"I'm sure the newspapers have written too much about too little," said Ethel. "I hope it won't make any difference about my finding work."

Frohman grinned. "Not at all." He jumped to his feet. Smoke circled his head. When not clenched in his teeth, his cigar was waved around like a wand. "The more headlines, the better. And you do look more and more like your mother, and there's the name . . ." His voice trailed off in thought. "There is a part in Annie Russell's new play, *Catherine*. Not much of a part, though."

Ethel didn't wait for him to change his mind. "Oh, thank you, Mr. Frohman. I would be pleased with anything."

That wasn't what she had meant to say at all, but she had

memories of another time in New York when she had gone from one casting office to another looking for work. She didn't want to burden Uncle Jack anymore.

"Be at the Garrick Theatre tomorrow at one," Frohman said.

When she arrived, Ethel found that it was indeed a small part. In a few minutes she had memorized her lines. The director told her that she would have to pay for two elaborate costumes out of her salary of thirty-five dollars a week. Ethel asked for an advance on that salary so she could check out of the Waldorf and into a boardinghouse within her budget. She was starting all over again, but she didn't mind. It was good to be home.

When Ethel made her entrance the first night of the play, she received a tremendous ovation, louder and longer than was given the stars of the performance. She suffered an agony of embarrassment. Only the notoriety of newspaper headlines had brought her to the attention of the public. She had no idea that her personal life in England could have been so advertised in her own country.

The star of the play, Annie Russell, insisted that Ethel be dropped from the cast, but Frohman would not hear of it. If people came to see Ethel in her brief appearance on stage, that was all the better. The record at the box office counted. Ethel had other ideas. She made up her mind that some-day — and she planned it would be soon — she would earn that applause for her acting. The names Barrymore and Drew were great because of talent; she would add luster to that heritage. It was the first time she had seriously considered the stage as more than a way to earn a livelihood.

10

The American newspapers would not leave Ethel's private life alone. They manufactured some of the most preposterous stories. There was a report that she had become engaged to a young socialite, Charles Witmore. The same day another paper announced that the lucky man was actor Ernest Lawford. Ethel suspected that Charles Frohman himself might be inventing some of the stories to keep her name in the news, but she had no proof. The publicity brought her small parts on the stage, but it was hard to make anybody believe she was serious about becoming an actress.

Ethel went to Frohman, demanding that he give her more challenging roles. The producer was amused at her audacity, but he was well aware that her name on the billboard assured a full house. Remembering that she had been able to play a woman of the world even four years before, he decided to let her take over the part of Stell de Gex in *His Excellency the Governor*. The part was given to Ethel on a trial basis, but she was assured an eight-week tour.

Ethel was delighted. This was more exciting than appearing as a simpering, empty-headed heroine mouthing insipid dialogue. The part called for her to portray a comedy adventuress. Again she got out the red wig and bought herself a spangled gown. If she was going to impress the critics with her acting, she must study the part, perfect the timing. Ethel remembered that her mother had mastered the technique of tossing a line away as if it meant nothing. This always brought more laughter than heavily stressing a comic line.

She could even quote some words that Georgie had spoken to a friend: "Be natural, so they don't see the wheels going around." Ethel began to understand the necessity of covering up the "wheels" in her own acting. She was really ahead of her time with her refreshing naturalness, for it was still fashionable to exaggerate gestures and speak the least important lines as if they were dramatic pronouncements. This style did not seem right to her, yet to be at ease with a role meant hard work and a thorough understanding of the part.

The result was successful. The critics were delighted. They began to print columns about Ethel's "surprising acting ability" without bannering the words with headlines proclaiming her the "Most Engaged Girl in America."

Ethel enjoyed surprising her public as much as astounding the critics. People still came to see the young girl who had conquered the hearts of England's nobility, and frequently, when Ethel was on tour, a local society leader would entertain her to bask in the reflected limelight.

One such gala took place in Detroit, where Ethel was to be received in one of the most fashionable homes in the area. Her curious hostess had invited a number of the handsomest and most elaborately dressed women of the city. When the door opened for the guest of honor, there stood Ethel, not the siren of the century or Stell de Gex of the flaming red hair, but a very young girl in somber velvet cut modestly to cover her from floor to throat.

A society editor reported:

No ornament relieved the almost puritan severity of costume save where strings of pearls shimmered above her high collar, no color showed save where the bloom of youth and health gleamed pink through clear, childishly soft cheeks. Big eyes that were luminous and appealing turned rapidly from one to another, as with the air of a debutante she stood beside her chaperone to receive necessary introductions. The actress was gone.

Or was she? Ethel was shy at times, yet she loved attention from her public and was perfectly capable of setting her own stage.

On her American tour, Ethel saved enough to afford another summer in England. Immediately she stepped, like Alice through the looking glass, into a world of her own, the glamorous social life she had known before. She moved from the Savoy Hotel to the home of a friend, the Duchess of Sutherland. Ethel had a chance to meet not only others interested in the theater but many literary greats as well, among them Max Beerbohm and G. K. Chesterton. When the Sutherlands moved their household from London to their castle in Scotland, Ethel went along. At Dunrobin Ethel met the young Winston Churchill, who was also added to her list of rumored suitors.

Still, by the end of the summer, Ethel was restless to return to America, hopeful she would find a play in which she could do more than sweep her train across the stage. Again she went to the office of Charles Frohman. He greeted her warmly with the surprising news that Clyde Fitch, then America's most successful playwright, had been writing a play with her expressly in mind. It was titled *Captain Jinks of the Horse Marines.*

Ethel was to play the part of Madame Trentoni, a famous European actress. When she comes to America, three young men of the Horse Marines decide to pool their resources and woo the young woman; the winner will divide her fortune with his two rivals. Captain Jinks, however, immediately falls in love with the heroine, and true love wins the day. Frohman himself was not too much impressed with the frothy bit of comedy Fitch had written, but perhaps because of this he was willing to entrust the role to young Ethel, whom he still considered a newcomer to the ranks of professional actresses.

The night of the tryout in Philadelphia, Ethel stood in the wings waiting for her entrance. She suddenly realized that the play very much depended upon her; it would stand or fall on her performance. She began to tremble. People had paid their money at the ticket window to see her. The cast, the producer, and the playwright were all waiting for her to prove her right to be called an actress. In an agony of terror, she was sure she was going to be sick. Her cue came. In a daze she moved forward, head lowered, afraid to look out toward the audience. Suddenly a voice from the gallery called out, "Speak up, Ethel. You Drews is all good actors!"

Her stage fright washed away. Ethel smiled and from then on caught the light mood so essential for the part. Her friends all congratulated her on a job well done. She herself felt she had been a success, but she waited anxiously to see the reviews in the papers the next morning. This was her first starring role.

She was horrified to learn how bad the reviews were. One critic went so far as to say, "If the young lady who plays Madame Trentoni had possessed beauty, charm, or talent, this play might have been a success." Quietly Ethel retreated to her hotel room and refused to see anyone. Yet she knew she must endure the agony of going on stage the following night and repeating the performance.

The theater was half full, and after one week Charles Frohman decided to send the cast on tour to salvage some of the expenses of the production. Clyde Fitch, the playwright, would not admit to failure. Already he had two plays on Broadway and wanted to set the unprecedented record of opening his third production. He insisted on a New York engagement. Ethel was frightened of certain failure, which could permanently damage her career, but she had no choice in the matter. Frohman scheduled the play at the Garrick Theater for a brief, two-week run.

The opening night was February 4, 1901. In Ethel's dressing room was a huge red apple, sent ahead of time by her Uncle Jack. Even her father had promised to come. She wished frantically that they would stay away. She dreamed hopefully that some emergency would rescue her from the humiliation of going on stage to face friends and family in a performance that had already been judged a failure.

For the first few moments on stage, she felt awkward and stiff. Then she thought, "How would Georgie or Mum mum have played the part?" Georgie would have been charming and gay; Mum mum would have commanded the attention of the audience by her personal magnetism. Ethel knew she must put sparkle into her part. At least she would try. Her voice took on rich contralto tones of confidence, and her performance finally drew thundering applause.

The next day's papers reported that the "curtain had been rung down amidst the clapping of hands, the beating of the floor with canes and umbrellas, and shouts of praise." The fickle public had changed their minds. They had fallen in love all over again with Ethel Barrymore. From that moment on, she was a star.

The play's run was extended to three months, then to six months. Every evening Ethel received a large bouquet of red roses from an unknown admirer. Newspaper reporters, artists, and photographers waited hopefully to find some item, some pose, for print. Young girls started to model themselves after Ethel, copying her hair style and the cut of her dresses. If they had been discerning, they might have realized that Ethel was being her natural self. Her hair was straight. She wore it that way, wound in a low knot at the back of her neck. Her hair was brown; that was the color that became popular. During the years when it had been necessary for Ethel to spend only a little money on her clothes, she had become accustomed to wearing black or white or grey, so that accessories would match and her outfits would not look so dated from year to year. These continued to be her choice of colors. At a time when ornateness of dress was most often overdone, Ethel often said that expensive fabric was not necessary. It was the way that a dress was cut and made and worn that made it stunning. Hopsacking could be made to look elegant if it was simple and understated.

Ethel's name blazed in electric lights over the theater marquee, but her glory did not seem to spoil her. She continued to live at Mrs. Wilson's boardinghouse, and her friends included not only the fashionable and the talented of the theater, but many unknowns who had befriended her in the past. Elroy Sheridan, the stage manager of many a Frohman production, and his wife often shared a supper table with Ethel at the restaurant around the corner from the theater. She had an imperious way with some whom she didn't know or like, but it was only natural that a young woman who had received so much public attention had to appear aloof to guard a bit of privacy.

To her father and brothers she gave generously: money, concern, attention. Maurice had become a constant worry. As Ethel's star was ascending on Broadway, Maurice's was dropping like a flaming comet. His behavior had become more and more erratic and eccentric. He had lost his last acting job not only because he was drinking and had become unable to remember his lines but also because on two occasions he had stopped in the middle of a performance to step to the footlights and harangue the audience about the evil practices of theatrical managers. When off stage, Maurice would brag that he had financing to build the largest theater in the world, which would cover many city blocks. He announced that only those actors who had appeared with him in vaudeville would ever be permitted to perform on this colossal stage. In Philadelphia he purchased twenty identical suits of clothes and refused to pay for any of them because the cut of one varied a fraction of an inch.

Ethel consulted with Maurice's close friend, August Thomas, and with their attorney. It was decided that the only solution was to commit Maurice to a mental hospital in the hopes that he could be brought back to sanity. Maurice was first admitted to Bellevue Hospital, where his mood changed from frenzy to incoherent docility. Later he was moved to a rest home on Long Island.

Maurice Barrymore's collapse had a profound effect on each of his children. Ethel rarely spoke of it to outsiders, yet she assumed the considerable financial burden of his care for the next four years. Lionel, who was the least like his father, decided to study for all the light romantic roles of drawing-room comedy that had made his father famous. He was extremely disappointed when he was passed aside and offered other parts, but fortunately they were of more dramatic substance and helped, not harmed, his career.

John Barrymore, who had inherited Maurice's outgoing, debonair love of life, was the most profoundly shocked of the three. The fear haunted him that he, too, would suffer such a nervous breakdown. Throughout John's life, Ethel struggled to shake his premonition that he would end his days in a mental hospital. Some of John's behavior tempted the public to side with his appraisal of his future rather than his sister's, but he never crossed the acceptable line of extremes.

Although Lionel was a year older than Ethel and had been engaged in the theater for almost as long as she had, his career had not progressed with equal sparkling success. He was lucky to find work for a week at a time. Frohman offered Ethel a large bonus for her achievement in *Captain Jinks,* but Ethel proposed a counteroffer. She would forgo the bonus if Frohman would find a part for Lionel. Frohman agreed, saying he was casting John Drew's next play, *The Mummy and the Humming Bird,* but that the only part available was that of an Italian organ grinder, which would require a convincing accent.

Lionel at once went to work to develop the role. He enlisted the help of not one, but three Italian waiters. He diligently kept at his practice for a month, becoming proficient enough to surprise even his family. The role also called for some frantic emotion. At the end of one of his scenes, he was to draw a knife from his belt, kiss it fiercely, and collapse in wild sobs in a chair as the curtain fell. At the dress rehearsal, Lionel wanted to impress Frohman and the director with his histrionics. Crying real tears, he threw himself toward the chair — and missed it completely.

Instead of responding with laughter or rage, Frohman quietly commented, "I'm glad you did that tonight, Barrymore, because now I know you won't do it again."

Lionel sheepishly scrambled to his feet, judged the distance from standing position to chair, and practiced it again and again until his body ached and his confidence returned.

On opening night Lionel gave an excellent performance. The critics announced that another Barrymore talent had been discovered — with the help of Ethel, it might be remembered. From then on Lionel had no problem finding choice roles. Even as a youth he preferred the off-beat character parts that gave him a chance to display his unusually intense acting talent.

Ethel also arranged for John's stage debut. While she was touring with her hit, *Captain Jinks of the Horse Marines,* one of the young men of the cast was notified that his mother had died. No understudy was available, so Ethel took it upon herself to wire John to meet them in Philadelphia. She sent him the script with instructions to memorize the part of one of the lieutenants while he was on the train.

John prepared for his first performance with the most casual care, arriving at the theater just in time to don his costume and respond to cue call. It became apparent all too soon that he had not learned his part, that in fact he had learned the wrong part. In the middle of one of his scenes he turned to a fellow actor and said, "I've blown up, old chap. Where do we go from here?"

He cheerfully improvised during the rest of the play, leaving the rest of the cast to flounder for themselves. Instead of being annoyed, Ethel stood in the wings doubled up with laughter. It had been customary for Ethel to take the first curtain call at the end of the play and then to bring the others out to share the applause. Somehow, in the mad confusion backstage on this night, John found himself greeting the audience alone as the curtain went up. He bowed low and then graciously went to the wings to bring on the rest of the cast. The audience thought it was all part of the act, and John's name was mentioned as a talented comedian. However, the regular cast was glad he was not called upon to repeat his performance the following night.

It was another year before John's formal debut took place. In the meantime he depended heavily on finances from his sister. She began to ignore his requests unless they were worded as the most dire emergency. During one such crisis, John went to the telegraph office with this message: "For Christ's sake, send me fifty dollars."

The clerk refused to send such a blasphemous message, but John explained that a friend of his named George W. Christ had taken ill and needed money. Of course, with the proper explanation, the message was sent.

Ethel never complained about these drains on her resources. Grandmother Drew and Uncle Jack had been the family protectors for a long time. Now she felt it was her turn. Somehow she never expected that either Lionel or John would step forward as head of the family. When they might have helped, her role was already established.

11

Whenever the strain of work or family worries overcame her, Ethel escaped to her beloved England. Her friends there greeted her as if she had left briefly for a weekend. Ethel learned to play golf near a castle rented for the summer by the Asquiths. Sir Herbert Asquith was at that time prime minister of England. Ethel sparkled at intimate little dinners attended by members of the peerage and of the world of letters. At twenty-two she took it for granted that such interesting things were happening to her. A touch of grandness came into her manner, but it was only natural considering the company she kept.

When Ethel returned to America, her public appointed her their own princess. Whether she liked it or not, Ethel's following was created because of her off-stage role; every young woman hoped that what had happened to Ethel could happen to her. But Ethel's prominence was ascribed more to her glamour and personality than to her acting ability. It bothered her that the roles she portrayed on the stage had never really tested her depth as an actress.

During a reunion she had with Sir Henry Irving, who had given her her first big role on the London stage, he said, "So you are a great star now."

Ethel answered, "No, not really. The critics say that I'm good and that I look all right, but that I'm always Ethel Barrymore."

Sir Henry smiled. "See to it that they never say anything else."

Now that Ethel had repolished the luster of the Barrymore name, it became easier for the family to gain employment, but Lionel was far from overjoyed by his career. He told one of his friends, "From the moment the audience shuffles in and the orchestra scrapes the overture, it is a nightmare. I may know my lines letter perfect in the privacy of my room, but there is always the terrifying possibility that I will forget them."

Lionel never did forget his lines, but his nervous condition made him decide that he would leave the stage forever. What profession was he to follow? He was a more serious artist than his brother John, and he also shared Ethel's love for music, having composed some of the pieces that were played during the intermissions of the Frohman plays. Either one of these creative professions would have pleased him more than the theater. He wrote Ethel about his decision, telling her he planned to take one more role to help finance his future.

Frohman arranged an all-Barrymore production. Lionel accepted the offer to play the title role of Pantaloon in the twin bill of plays by James M. Barrie; Ethel would star in *Alice Sit-By-the-Fire* while John had a supporting part in that play. It was the only time in their lives that all three Barrymores shared a stage together.

Lionel still complained that he was in terror of forgetting his lines, although his performance did not show his anxiety, and the critics praised his magnificent portrayal of an old man. They said that he was able to bridge the years even with his voice. When the play closed, Lionel again let it be known that he was deserting the family theatrical tradition; he was going to study art. Ethel sympathized and even offered to send him a small stipend every month if he wished to test and improve his talent in Paris.

One of Ethel's friends at the time remarked that no man would ever be able to support her if she continued her generous gestures and extravagant living. Another answered that Lionel and John could easily support Ethel and her future husband on the money Ethel had given to her brothers.

Ethel continued to be offered starring roles in New York. She returned from her regular London vacation to act in a new play, *Sunday,* about a young foundling who was brought up by four miners in the West. Ethel had to hide her slightly aristocratic British accent with a western drawl. It seemed to satisfy her public, for she forever became known for one line in this play, a line that she improvised.

During the second act of *Sunday,* the character Ethel was portraying has been returned to her real family and has received a letter composed by the four miners. As she reads it to her aunt, she comes to a personal passage. The stage directions called for the character to stop and run off stage. During rehearsal, Ethel felt that this was too abrupt an exit and suggested to the director that at least one line be added before she ran to the wings.

"Go ahead and try it your way," said the director.

As Ethel paused in mid-sentence in her reading of the letter, her aunt said, "Go on, Sunday."

Ethel turned toward the audience and thoughtfully drawled, "That's all there is, there isn't any more."

On opening night the line was left intact, and when the scene ended, the audience burst into applause. Much to her annoyance, that line of dialogue became virtually Ethel's trademark, and no Barrymore imitation would have been complete without it.

When she was in London, Ethel saw a performance of a new play, *Lady Frederick,* written by Somerset Maugham. She persuaded Charles Frohman to schedule it for an opening in September of 1909. He agreed, on the condition that she would come back early for rehearsal. During the two weeks that Ethel spent preparing the part, she met a handsome young man named Russell Griswold Colt. He was two years her junior, but a charming son of the millionaire president of the United States Rubber Company. Colt was well educated and well traveled, had a sense of humor, and played an excellent game of bridge. He had plenty of time to sharpen this latter ability because he had nothing much to do except travel between the fashionable resorts of Newport and Palm Beach.

The young man had a classic profile that could match any in the Barrymore family, although his mouth seemed a bit effeminate with an unnatural pout; he was always impeccably dressed in the height of fashion. Ethel was warned that he had a roving eye for the ladies, but before their marriage Russell was a devoted suitor, proud that he had won Ethel himself without the money or backing of his father.

Ethel fell in love with Russell Colt, but she decided that she would not announce her engagement this time until she was absolutely sure she felt a lasting emotion. In the meantime she continued her rehearsals for *Lady Frederick.* Again it was a light comedy, with the only switch being that Ethel was to appear on stage without her cloak of glamour. The script called for her to disenchant a suitor by arranging for him to learn the artificial mysteries of her beauty preparations. Ethel played the role to the hilt, appearing on stage in rumpled dressing gown, hair frowsy, without makeup. In the play, the young man watches as the heroine adds quantities of hairpieces to her own tresses. As she paints on the bloom of youth, his feelings change, and he runs off stage while the audience howls with laughter.

This performance did not discourage Ethel's real suitor. Their courtship went on without interruption. When Ethel opened *Lady Frederick* in New York, Russell bought a front-row seat for the entire run. If his seat was empty she would hurry backstage between acts, pick up the phone in her dressing room, and find the circuit already connected with Russell on the other end. Huge bouquets of flowers from Ethel's fiancé turned her dressing room into a spring bower.

The engagement was announced on March 9. Immediately Russell's father, Colonel Samuel Colt, asked Ethel to come to see him. He told her that because of a mild panic on Wall Street he and his son were destitute. This was far from the truth, although their income had been curtailed. Ethel at once vowed that she was marrying for love alone and assured him that, no matter what happened, she made enough to support the two of them. This seemed to satisfy her prospective father-in-law, and the date of the wedding was set. As an afterthought, Ethel added that she thought it would be a good thing if Russell had some kind of a job. The Colonel agreed and said that he would immediately look into the mechanics of making Russell a junior partner in the brokerage house of H. L. Horton and Company.

On March 14 the two were married, as secretly as possible, at the home of a priest in Hyde Park, New York. John Barrymore and Russell's brother, Roswell Colt, were the only witnesses. The following day Ethel returned to the play.

The Colts' honeymoon trip was the tour of *Lady Frederick,* which took them all the way to California. Destitute or not, Colonel Colt provided the use of a private railway car as a wedding present.

When the newlyweds returned, Charles Frohman announced that he felt it was time that Ethel took on more serious dramatic plays, which was just what she had been wanting for some time. However, Ethel was expecting a dramatic event in her own life in a few months — the birth of her first child. Ethel and Russell took a house for the summer in Greenwich, Connecticut. It was a time of pleasurable laziness for Ethel. She curtailed most of her social engagements; Russell occasionally commuted to Wall Street to see what was going on, but with the usual signs of irresponsibility, he never kept to a schedule. When asked by a friend, "What train do you take?" his honest answer was, "I usually miss the 10:37."

Both Lionel and John were frequent visitors to the Colts' Connecticut house. That year, though, John, Ethel's favorite, was scheduled for a theatrical engagement in San Francisco. He arrived just in time for the terrible earthquake and fire that practically destroyed that great city. John had come in late from a party and was lying on top of his bed in his hotel room in full evening dress. At 5:15 in the morning, he was thrown from his bed by the first of the violent shock waves. He picked himself up and rushed outside, hoping to make his way toward the Bay, where he thought it would be safer. Before he had pushed his way more than a block in that direction, an army officer handed him a shovel and told him to dig.

When Uncle Jack heard his nephew's dramatic account of his part in the holocaust, his comment was that only a convulsion of nature could have awakened John Barrymore at that hour in the morning and only the United States Army could have put him to work.

In the fall the Colts moved back to New York, renting the lavish Belmont residence on Thirty-fourth Street. Although Ethel was not expecting her baby until January, a nurse, Mrs. Frings, was hired to take charge of the expected occupant of the beautifully decorated nursery. One day in November, the nurse stopped by to ask Ethel some questions about buying items for the layette. Out of courtesy she casually asked her employer how she had been feeling.

Ethel answered, "I feel fine now, but in the night I had a sort of pain and took some Jamaica ginger."

"I think you should call your doctor," Mrs. Frings suggested.

"I'm really fine," Ethel insisted. "Besides, I am going to spend the day with friends in Garden City."

"Not today, Mrs. Colt. You'll be having your baby sooner than you expect. I'm calling the doctor now," said the concerned Mrs. Frings.

Ethel did not argue. When Dr. Danforth arrived, he agreed with Mrs. Frings's prediction. That night, November 28, Ethel's son, a premature baby weighing only three and one-half pounds, was born. The doctor did not believe in incubators, and Mrs. Frings probably saved the baby's life with her constant care and by arranging an electric heating pad under the baby's crib mattress. Ethel's own health was excellent.

Photographers were immediately knocking on her door, and soon pictures in all the newspapers showed Ethel in her new maternal role. Her public did not desert her, although she had reached thirty and had added a new plumpness to her fashionable figure. The new mother was still Queen Ethel.

Colonel Colt was even more impressed with the new arrival than was Russell. The baby was christened Samuel Pomeroy Colt in honor of the child's great-grandfather, the inventor of the famous .45-caliber revolver. Even before the christening, Ethel was reading play scripts. Again Frohman suggested that Ethel was ready to forsake comedy and try deeper material. It was decided she would open in Pinero's *Mid-Channel*. European critics had called the play distressingly unpleasant, for in it, a wealthy English couple spend all three acts angrily screaming at each other.

To make entertainment out of such a somber vehicle was a real test of Ethel's skill. The play went on tour briefly, and Ethel called home every day to talk to the nurse. Russell was rarely home; he cared little about Ethel's theatrical career, and now that the honeymoon was over he spent more and more of his time with his own circle of friends. Colonel Colt suggested that in the summer, when Ethel was free from her stage schedule, the couple might enjoy owning a house in the country, which would be his present to them.

Ethel was delighted. She at once set about finding the perfect location. She followed up dozens of real estate leads, but the houses were either too inaccessible or too poorly constructed. Her final choice was a lovely old home in Mamaroneck, just twenty miles from the city. Russell didn't like it. He thought she was crazy, for the house was painted barn red with black shutters. The interior was dark, and the mantel was a horror of wooden curlicues.

To Ethel, who could visualize a change of paint and a bit of remodeling, the place was charming. It was surrounded by ten acres of orchard land. It would be a wonderful place to raise a family. It would be a place for her to unpack permanently for the first time in her life. Ethel had visited in lovely homes before but never had owned such a place herself. Russell shrugged away his indifference and left Ethel to furnish her nest.

In the fall it was time for her to go back to the theater. Frohman did not have any play that particularly pleased her, so she decided to try a stint of vaudeville. At the time Maude Adams, Sarah Bernhardt, Uncle Jack — all the great stars of the day — were appearing in short dramatic sketches on vaudeville programs. Ethel chose to open in Barrie's one-act drama, *The Twelve-Pound Look.* Comedians, acrobats, and musicians shared the billing, but Ethel never felt herself above them.

"There is so much to learn," she said. "All performers must be perfectionists. If the slackwire artist falls he may lose his life. If I stumble only my reputation is at stake, but I must be as good in my job as he is in his. Vaudeville audiences are different. They are exacting. Nothing must ever be slurred for them. To be perfect night after night takes study."

Ethel did more than an average amount of studying. She rehearsed the cast using a method all her own. A thin black curtain was hung across the stage. The actors rehearsed their lines while Ethel sat out front judging from their voices alone whether they were interpreting the characters correctly. After the dialogue had been polished, she had them do the play again in pantomime to assure that their body actions were both graceful and dramatically true to the point of the play. For this direction Ethel received the handsome sum of three thousand dollars a week.

In the summer the family again returned to their lovely

estate at Mamaroneck. There were times when Ethel and her husband felt a close bond to each other. They both loved sports, and Ethel accompanied Russell to every baseball game within commuting distance, as far as Philadelphia and Pittsburgh. Ethel genuinely loved the game and did not attend just to keep her husband company. They watched polo games and tennis matches, even boxing matches. When Ethel was asked why she never became a football fan, her answer was simply that she always had a Saturday matinee. The sport she liked most of all was swimming; whenever she found both time and surf she would enjoy the water.

Ethel discovered that she was again expecting a baby, but it barely slowed her schedule of performances. On April 3, 1912, her second child, a little girl, was born. While Ethel was still unconscious, the reporters called and were given the news by the doctor. When asked the baby's name, the doctor said, "Why, Ethel, of course." Ethel, senior, hadn't planned it so, but after the announcement had been made she decided not to change the name. However, little Ethel became known in the family as Sister or Sissy.

A year and a half later, in September of 1913, Jackie was born. Two hours after that delivery, Ethel was on the phone with Charles Frohman.

"I have an awfully nice little boy," she said.

"Why, Ethel, that's not possible. I just saw you yesterday," the producer answered.

"We've named him John," she continued.

"When, when?" Frohman sputtered.

"Two hours ago." Ethel laughed at Frohman's utter confusion.

He exclaimed, "It is impossible for you to be talking."

"How strange," said Ethel. "I thought that's what I was

doing. I just wanted you to know that I will be ready for re-hearsals very soon."

Ten days after Jackie came into the world, Ethel was rehearsing *Tante* on the stage of the Empire Theater.

Ethel always had a competent nurse to care for her children, but she remained a devoted mother. When Sister came down with a high temperature and what was thought to be croup, Ethel rushed the baby to a specialist. The doctor gave Ethel the terrifying news that the little girl was suffering from diphtheria. Ethel went directly to the hospital with the child and stayed until the danger had passed.

Colonel Colt spoiled his grandchildren indulgently. Long before little Jackie could possibly do more than hurl toys across the room, his grandfather presented him with an elaborate fort guarded by an army of toy soldiers dressed in the uniforms of every country in the world.

The time had come when others were thinking of soldiering and guns. World War I, a war that was to affect all Americans deeply, had started in Europe. Ethel would be particularly affected.

12

It seemed strangely unreal for Americans to know that across what had been a peaceful ocean barrier men were killing and dying. With so many ties in England, Ethel was afraid to read the newspapers. Several of her closest friends were lost in the early days of the war. Dick Davis, who went to Brussels as a war correspondent in April, 1915, was killed a year later. Uncle Sidney's son, Sidney Rankin Drew, joined the Lafayette Escadrille and was shot down in flames.

Yet the greatest loss to Ethel was her good friend and manager Charles Frohman. Ethel depended upon the rotund little man more than she realized, for personal advice as well as professional help. When he told her of his planned business trip to England, she tried to dissuade him.

"You'd have me miss that lovely crossing, Mrs. Colt?" Frohman said. "How many times have you dashed over for a breath of foggy air?"

Ethel smiled. "I'd give anything to be there now too, but it's foolish to tempt chance during wartime."

Frohman ignored her warning. "I'll bring home a tin of tea biscuits for you, how's that?"

Although Ethel was playing in Boston at the time, she decided to come to New York and wish Frohman "bon voyage"

before he boarded the *Lusitania*. Six days later Ethel received
the tragic news that the ship had been torpedoed by a Ger-
man submarine. Most of the ship's crew and passengers were
lost, Charles Frohman among them. Ethel was shocked. She
kept repeating, "Mr. Frohman, Mr. Frohman. He can't be
gone. I saw him last week." Only hard work could help her
put his name out of her mind.

To the surprise of his friends and family, Russell Colt vol-
unteered as an ambulance driver in France. When the
United States joined the war, he returned to apply for a
commission in the army. He suddenly developed a sense of
responsibility and dedication. Ethel was alone a great deal
of the time. There wasn't much a woman could do but sit
and wait, yet she appeared in benefits and pageants for war
relief charities. The first time she was to go on stage for
recitation, she panicked. It was hard enough to live through
an opening night performance in the theater, where she
could lose herself in a part, but she found it even worse to
appear in front of an audience as herself.

She tried to keep busy. One of her favorite parts was as
Marguerite in *The Lady of Camelias*. At the very end of the
play, the heroine dies as her lover cries out, "Marguerite, my
love, come back to me." Immediately the scene blacks out.
At every performance, when the house lights were turned
on, the audience began sniffling and blowing their noses.
Two of Ethel's friends, Louise Wanamaker and Mary War-
burton, came to every matinee. They brought a supply of
men's handkerchiefs and cried through the whole play.
Sometimes, when they were at the Follies or a party, they
would rush their friends to the theater to see the last act of
yet another performance.

"Oh, let's see her die," became one of the family jokes, or
"wheezes," as Ethel called them.

The war was barely won when Ethel became involved in another battle. The actors' union, Actors' Equity, had gone on strike; all but one of the New York theaters were closed. Ethel had known nothing about the planning of the strike, but once the wheels were put in motion, she knew she would do anything she could to further the cause of the strikers. There was much unfairness in the theatrical system. Actors were required to rehearse a play for at least four weeks before an opening without any pay at all. If a play closed on tour, the cast was frequently stranded in some little town without any funds at all. Supporting actors and actresses paid for their own costumes, while the stars had no expenses at all and received amazingly disproportionate salaries.

Ethel was at the peak of her career and had nothing to gain from such a strike. In fact, she was losing playing time as long as the theaters were closed. She hadn't the least idea what she could do, but one day she called for her car and ordered the driver to take her to strike headquarters on Forty-fifth Street. As her car turned in from Sixth Avenue and headed toward Broadway, she saw a huge crowd blocking the way. She was puzzled but decided to get out of her car and push her way through the mass of people. She had only two blocks to walk.

Immediately someone recognized her. "It's Ethel, Ethel Barrymore." Shouts rippled outward like rings of water. At the same time the crowd surged toward her. She was frightened and turned to run, but she couldn't move. A tall, bearded man by her side tried to stop the shoving and pushing.

"To the strike headquarters," someone shouted.

Ethel was carried along with the crowd like a cork bobbing in a riptide. Once she tripped, but there was nowhere to fall. She was bruised and out of breath by the time they reached the steps of the old brownstone building that was the strike headquarters. Someone put a flag in her hand and shouted, "We can't lose with Ethel."

Ethel trembled, but now she was not afraid. The strikers were calling for her help, her leadership; she was needed. For a moment she felt like Joan of Arc. Someone carried her up the steps into the house and lifted her to a table. A woman was crying, kissing the hem of her skirt. "It's all right now. We'll win," the woman said.

Ethel, moved nearly to tears herself, said simply, "I'm with you."

The crowd had found their champion, the beautiful aristocrat whose interests would seem to have been allied with the theatrical establishment. Instead she was joining with the little people. Ethel went further than just lending her words to the cause. When the strikers began to go hungry (and, being actors, many of them already were), Ethel organized benefit stage performances to raise money for their relief. She enlisted the help of some of the biggest names of the theater. The stars of these productions were treated just like the chorus, having to share dressing rooms, rushing on stage for one-line parts, then helping to move scenery backstage. Ethel produced three different star-studded productions that played to standing-room-only audiences. With the help of her Uncle Jack, Ethel sponsored a ball at the Astor Hotel that raised money for the strikers' fund.

The public was on the side of the actors too, and the opposition was forced to give in. They did so on all points. Ethel was appointed as one of the group that signed a five-year pact between actors and management. It was a triumph for Ethel, but she had earned the ill feelings of Alf Hayman, who had taken over Charles Frohman Incorporated. He sulked and he grumbled, but he still found an occasional tearjerker for Ethel to play in.

Ironically, although she was so frequently able to help others, no one seemed to be able to bring real happiness and comfort to Ethel. For eleven years she had tried to make a success of her marriage, but her husband paid no attention to the children and rarely joined her at any social gatherings. Ethel paid most of the household expenses. Finally, even she felt she couldn't continue, and a divorce was granted by the courts.

Ethel's health also suffered. Although the public did not know it, she was beginning to suffer from arthritis, which in later years made it difficult for her to move about. Ethel had a maid to care for her, but her children were now in boarding school and she was alone more than ever. Sister was attending the same convent school where Ethel had been so happy as a young girl. Sister Julie de Saint Esprit, who had first greeted Ethel on the steps of Notre Dame Academy, was there to greet her daughter, too. It made Ethel realize that the years were passing.

Ethel had reached the age when most actresses would have been willing to rest on their laurels and retire to a life of relaxation. But rest was something Ethel had never known and obviously did not cherish. She was always looking for a good play. Lionel had given up his painting and was working in the movies. John was making a success as Hamlet. Ethel turned to Shakespeare for an ill-fated production of *Romeo and Juliet,* but she was middle-aged when she attempted the youthful role. Too late, she realized that drawing-room comedy or romantic tragedy was her real forte.

Even as great a star as Ethel Barrymore had to face hard times, and for the next several productions Ethel suffered at the hands of the critics. *A Royal Fandango* was closed after a poor run, but Ethel and the public were not to forget the debut of a new young actor named Spencer Tracy. He had only a few lines to say but was dreadfully nervous about them. Before his entrance Ethel gave him the encouraging advice, "Relax. That's all you have to do. Just relax. It'll all be the same in a hundred years."

Ethel often couldn't follow her own words of wisdom. Invariably she was stricken with paralyzing stage fright on opening night, yet she had a wonderful command over her audience. Her brother John once commented after seeing one of Ethel's performances that he had never once heard a cough from the audience.

She told him, "But I don't let them cough."

"You don't? But how?" John asked.

"I just turn on something inside myself and they don't dare cough."

Ethel more and more became the great lady of the stage whom no one dared approach, yet she had reached that delicate age when it was difficult to maintain the glamour and youth of her starring days. She was now a woman of fifty; on the far side of the footlights she could easily pass for ten years younger, but the roles for a mature woman were not the leading parts. Ethel's confidence and perhaps her vanity were bruised. She hid herself from her public. Instead of walking down the street or being driven by a chauffeur, she now took taxis as a way of shielding herself from the gaze of strangers. Many felt that her aloofness was fostered by snobbery. It could more aptly have been described as a return to shyness.

Now she easily became upset by criticism, criticism that in the past she had considered to be beneath her and had ignored. She shunned the company of even her closest friends. It was a time of bitter loneliness for a woman who had been the toast of two continents, yet she never lost her sense of humor. After one matinee, her stage manager knocked on her door to tell her that a lady was calling who had gone to school with her. Ethel's immediate answer was, "Very well, wheel her in."

Her closest companion was her cousin, Georgie Drew Mendum, who frequently, thanks to Ethel's kindness, appeared in small roles in whatever play Ethel was performing. John and Lionel were now spending most of their time making movies on the West Coast, but Ethel disdained that medium, feeling it did not offer the same challenge as the stage.

During one of the few family get-togethers, Ethel delivered a lengthy sermon to her brothers, criticizing them for their desertion of the stage for the Hollywood trash she said they were helping to foster. In the middle of her speech, she looked at her watch and said, "Hurry, Georgie, we'll be late for the theater."

"Come now," John said, "you can surely stay for an after-dinner brandy."

Ethel insisted that they leave at once.

John turned to his brother and in mock seriousness said, "Lionel, how tragic it is we have given up the fabulous stage for the unspeakably low labor of the movies. Here are these two ladies going to work carrying on the family tradition while we are forced to sit on the patio and sip brandy. We must try not to be envious."

Ethel turned a furious look on her brothers, swept out of the room, and would not speak to either of them for more than a month.

In spite of Ethel's dwindling income, she continued to live in the style to which she had become accustomed. Although starring roles on Broadway did not come so frequently, she could usually find someone to back a company to tour one of her past hits. In Denver in July, 1931, she went through a puzzling performance, forgetting her cues and stumbling on stage. Between acts she was in a panic backstage. "I think I am losing my mind. I cannot remember a thing." The next evening she regained her composure, but a week later her problems returned. The papers hinted that she was under the influence of alcohol, but to anyone who knew Ethel, this explanation was ridiculous. The family was worried about her, insisting she see a doctor. She would not listen to their suggestions.

Finally Ethel was persuaded to take a week's leave of absence to visit her brother John in California. When unpacking her belongings, John noticed that she carried several bottles of an ordinary drugstore remedy to calm nerves. He hid them, and as soon as Ethel stopped her self-prescribed dosage, she returned to her normal, healthy self. However, no newspaper bothered to retract its insinuations.

Ethel might have followed her own advice and remained on the stage, but now, during the depression years, a generous offer from Hollywood lured her to the screen capital. A new career was waiting.

13

In June, 1932, all three Barrymores agreed to appear in the same picture, *Rasputin and the Empress*. At once the Hollywood press agents began to reel off reams of copy on the "Royal Family of the Theater." How would the three temperamental stars ever be able to get along on one movie set? Ethel had become so used to receiving the homage of top billing that many considered she had overdone her imperious ways. John was irresponsible but talented, and Lionel was forever trying to rewrite his own scripts.

Lionel himself was quoted as saying, "What poor unsuspecting maniac of a director is going to take on that job?"

When Ethel set out for the West Coast by train, John suggested she get off the train in Pasadena to avoid the crowds of reporters who were bound to be waiting for her in Hollywood. Some unkind remarks were made that John did not want his sister to get the first break of publicity releases. Whether this was true or not, John was on hand to greet his sister, and at least two reporters were beside him. One of the newsmen asked Ethel if she was worried about appearing in the same film with two such expert scene-stealers as her brothers.

John quickly stepped forward. "You need not worry about Mrs. Colt. Our sister will be standing right before the camera in front of us."

"And how do you rate your brother John's acting ability?" was another question.

Ethel's answer was, "Excellent when he isn't profiling himself through a role, and, of course, Lionel is the best living actor of character parts there is." The public was willing to agree.

Except for some time spent before cameras in 1918, Ethel knew nothing about the techniques of movie making. On her first day in California, John managed to give Ethel some good advice. "Get Bill Daniels," he told her.

"And who is he?" Ethel asked.

"Garbo's photographer. He'll make you look like the Mona Lisa."

Ethel surprised the producer, Irving Thalberg, by demanding the services of the famous photographer. Thalberg, who had hoped that at least one Barrymore could be guided by his own advice, could only grant her request.

Ethel had brought her three grown children with her on her trip to California, and her agent rented a lavish home in Beverly Hills for her short stay. She had been firm about insisting that her part in the film be completed within eight weeks, since she had prior acting commitments on the stage in New York. The production crew began to panic when they realized the script was unsatisfactory, and Charles MacArthur, a good friend of Ethel, was persuaded to step in and take charge of the writing. He barely managed to stay ahead of the actors.

The story itself was about the wicked doings of the Russian monk Rasputin, played by Lionel, who was supposed to have kept the Czarina, Ethel, under his hypnotic power with promises that he could cure her sickly son. Prince Paul, played by John, comes to the rescue and kills the monk. The murder scene in the film goes on and on, with John first using poison, then trying to push Lionel in a fireplace. During the struggle, John hits Lionel across the face with a poker and finally drags him outside in the snow to push his head in an ice-filled stream, drowning him.

"A delightful part," John remarked, but Lionel really had the best role of the three. With his beard and his maniacal laugh, he was the only one who could "ham up" his performance and have it seem a logical part of the plot. Ethel had little to do except look stately and distressed; and except for the one long murder scene, John stood around looking handsome, making sure his left profile was facing the camera.

Lionel, the only member of the family who had never known any members of the Russian nobility, spent hours of time studying the period and the characters. He came up with his own suggestions for change, from such details as the fact that Rasputin did not wear sandals — he wore boots — to a discovery of mistaken dates for historical events in the script. It was all very helpful but frustrating for the time schedule.

The film bred many wonderful quotes, and the picture itself became known as *Disputin and the Empress*. Once a studio photographer saw John and Ethel sitting near each other but not speaking. He suggested that John lean over to tell Ethel something so that the picture would look more natural. John reportedly said, "Tell Ethel something? I should say not, but I will ask her something."

Although it seemed that the film might be an excellent opportunity for the Barrymores to get together for a folksy family reunion, each one seemed to be busy on the set at different times, and the rushed schedule left very little time for socializing. It is also probable that although all three of them held the greatest respect for each other's professional talents, family ties were not strong. Over the years each had grown used to going his own separate way.

The filming was finished in breathless time, and Ethel rushed off to the East to escape the glaring, gaudy, unreal Hollywood she claimed she detested.

The next year, 1933, the middle of the depression, was one of the worst in Ethel's life. It was the first time in her career that she had been out of work for a whole year. What money she had earned in Hollywood had been consumed by lavish expenses, and to make it worse, the federal government pressed a claim against her for unpaid taxes. Although Ethel must often have despaired, none of her friends or family ever heard her complain about her reverses. The public learned of Ethel's problems only because she was forced to appear in court to ask for release of a small amount from her children's trust fund.

What had happened to all her money? Accountants came to look at her books. She had not squandered it on jewels or a gaudy wardrobe, but she had lived a royal life, keeping a staff of cooks, maids, gardeners, and a chauffeur even when her income fluctuated radically. She was not one to be practical, but then neither were her brothers. Lionel claimed to be "bewildered by anything that smacked of a decimal point," and John put even Ethel's extravagances to shame. At least she didn't maintain a yacht with a crew of ten.

In fact, Ethel was the only one of the three to attempt a conversion to economical living. She refused to sell her home in Mamaroneck, but she did board it up temporarily, moving

into a rather small, unfashionable — by Barrymore stan-
dards — hotel on upper Broadway. Her outward manner
was regal, but there were days and nights of fear.

It was hard, nearly impossible, for a woman who had been
such a great star to accept the fact that she was through.
The sound of silence was terrifying, as though her life's work
had been forgotten by all. Ethel tried to regain her confidence and some security once more by appearing in a vaudeville revival of *The Twelve-Pound Look,* but the play was
dated, and the reviews were scorching.

Ethel became unusually sensitive to criticism and would
pick a quarrel in her own defense. She acquired a reputation
for arrogance, yet she said to her friend Adela St. John,
"When life knocks you to your knees, which it always does
and always will at some time, well, that's the best position to
pray, isn't it?"

Since she had left the convent, so many years ago, she had
slipped from her habit of attending church regularly. Now
that she needed help, however, she drew strength from that
inner faith kindled in her days as a schoolgirl. Little by little,
with the help of prayer, she began to regain her strength.
She made her debut on radio by giving some readings from
one of her favorite plays, *The Kingdom of God*. It was before
a microphone that she announced her retirement from the
stage, saying that it was time for her to help young people
who aspired to a theatrical career; she would give classes in
speech and dramatics at her summer home in Mamaroneck.
She was deluged with requests for dramatic coaching, but
before she could give the first class, she signed a contract for
a twenty-six-week series of radio programs. She would revive
plays in which she had acted on Broadway. "There's no such
thing as an old lady's voice. Physical fitness and artistry can

bridge the gap of years," she said, and she proved it to be true.

Ethel began to make a slight recovery from her financial difficulties and made a settlement with the Internal Revenue Service. Finally, she began to emerge from her shell. She was happiest about being offered a stage role in the Theater Guild's production of *The Ghost of Yankee Doodle,* a play about a wealthy family of American liberals trying to adjust themselves to the spirit of the times. The play was not very successful, but again Ethel earned her red apple and rave notices. "The patrician tossing of the head, the flashing eyes, and the quiet grace of the celebrated Barrymore style made the play what it was," one reviewer said.

A member of the cast described her magnetism like this: "She could be playing a scene with you, seemingly looking into the innermost depths of your eyes, yet she would immediately notice if someone moved on the other side of the stage. Her flashing eyes could silence, terrify, any offender, yet she would not permit anyone to watch her in the wings."

The play lasted for only a brief run, but because of her success in the leading role, Ethel was offered another excellent part in *White Oaks.* The director timidly called Miss Barrymore on the phone and asked if she would be willing to play the part of a woman more than a hundred years old.

Ethel, then fifty-nine years old, answered, "I'd be perfectly delighted to. That's just what I feel."

Ethel's interpretation of the character again won approval. A reporter from the *New York Times* came backstage to see her and was amazed to be greeted by a tall, graceful woman with few facial lines to hint at age, instead of the limping, disreputable old woman whom he had just seen on the stage.

"Don't you use makeup?" he asked her.

"Not much," she replied. "My grandmother taught me this. I whiten my own teeth to make them look false. I depend on facial expression to do the rest. After all, the purpose of acting is to create the impression of youth or age, good or evil, happiness or sorrow."

Ethel still waited for a play that would combine a good character part with dramatic fire, yet would also be of current interest and relevant to the times. She knew she had found it when she read the script of *The Corn Is Green* by Emlyn Williams. She saw it as a simple play about a simple Englishwoman with a gift for teaching. It should be played in low key with the right touch of warmth and humility. Ethel rehearsed her part over and over, honing every line to perfection. On opening night when the final curtain was lowered, the theater rocked with applause. This time she received a bushel of apples from her brothers.

The Corn Is Green was one of the greatest hits of the American theater, surely the greatest of the 1940 season. Alexander Woollcott said that Ethel was serene, gentle, more beautiful than ever. Success had come at a crucial time in her life, rekindling her confidence and wiping away any of her thoughts of retirement.

14

Ethel's success again gave her the opportunity to throw herself into her work to help her forget the news of the day. The unbelievable events at Pearl Harbor sent the country to war, and Ethel's two sons went into the army.

In February, 1941, the National Broadcasting Company devoted a program to the fortieth anniversary of Ethel Barrymore's opening in *Captain Jinks of the Horse Marines*. Tributes were spoken by Louis B. Mayer, Helen Hayes, Alexander Woollcott, and Ethel's brothers, Lionel and John. Congratulatory mail swamped her hotel room.

Although she might have acted *The Corn Is Green* to full houses in New York, Ethel urged the producers to send the play on tour. The company played every city in the United States and then went straight back to New York to be booked again. For more than two years, Ethel kept to her exhausting schedule.

While she was in San Francisco, an executive of RKO Pictures asked her to read the movie script of *None but the Lonely Heart*. She liked the part of the elderly lady who ran a rummage shop in the seamy quarter of London, but she was still committed to the road tour. RKO felt she was so important to the part that they agreed to pay all the company's salaries during the time Ethel was making the picture and to reimburse theater owners for the cancellations. Still, Ethel had a hard time mastering the part of the destitute old lady. The director described the problem: "How do you make Queen Ethel into a frump? She wears her crushed old hat like a tiara."

Perseverance was the answer. Ethel played the scenes time after time until her shoulders slumped and she caught the mood of despair everyone wanted. She received the Academy Award in 1944 for this performance. However, she was more proud of the fact that only one hour elapsed between the time the last scene was filmed and the moment she boarded a train to resume her tour in *The Corn Is Green.*

Now Ethel softened her attitude toward Hollywood, for she was given the preferential treatment due her. Movies, she thought, "could be just like the stage, as subtle, and about things that matter." It was not long before she decided to settle in southern California permanently.

But "settle" was not yet a word that applied to Ethel. Again she went on tour with *The Corn Is Green.* In Boston she received a long-distance call from Lionel following her matinee performance. The call was put through to the box office, and Ethel at once had a sense of foreboding that something was wrong. She rushed from her dressing room to the office. In her haste she fell, but, scrambling to her feet again, she hobbled to the phone. Lionel had called to tell her John was dead. He had contracted bronchial pneumonia but had expressly forbidden Lionel to call their sister, not wanting to interrupt her tour. With the complications of already poor health, John had never recovered.

Ethel looked around her blankly. It was not possible that her little brother, the great Hamlet, the gallant hero, the sharp wit, would speak his lines no more. Her eyes were dry, but her lips trembled. Outwardly the family had not been close to one another, but emotionally they had been mutually dependent. Now the first tie was broken. John had been the first to go. Who would be next? She turned to go back to her dressing room, but a shooting pain stabbed up her leg. She could not put any weight on her foot.

The young man who had called her to the phone carried her to her dressing room. A doctor confirmed Ethel's fears. "You've broken a bone in your ankle, Miss Barrymore. You will have to have a cast."

"That's impossible. Not tonight," Ethel said. "My brother would not have me miss this performance. He did not call me when I might have gone to him."

The doctor hesitated. "I can tape your ankle, but you should be off your feet."

"I will be off my feet when the performance is over."

The evening papers carried word of John Barrymore's death. When Ethel made her entrance on the stage that night, the audience gave her a thunderous ovation. She stood silently with her head bowed, knowing for whom the applause was intended.

Only after the performance did she allow her foot to be properly encased in a cast.

At the time of John's death, Lionel also was struggling to regain his strength. Sometime earlier he had been working at home in his studio, sketching on a heavy, metal-edged drafting table. He leaned on it, upset it, tripped, and fell. When he tried to get up, he felt a stab of pain that took his breath away. He was taken to the hospital and immediately strung up in traction. He was furious. Immobility was something he could not tolerate. He let everyone within shouting distance know that he would rather be dead. Then he remembered a remark made by his brother only a few months before: "Die? I should say not, old fellow. No Barrymore would allow such a conventional thing to happen to him."

Ethel came to see Lionel frequently but failed miserably in her attempts to cheer him up. "It's fine for you to smile," Lionel ranted. "You can stand in front of an audience and take a bow."

Finally, after everyone's patience was almost gone, Lionel was back on his feet again. His next picture was *Saratoga,* with Clark Gable and Jean Harlow. When the filming was almost completed, he tripped over a sound cable and snapped his hip again. Once more he was put in a rack of pulleys, but this time recovery did not mean he was back on his feet. The bones mended, but he could not walk. Lionel, then one of Hollywood's greatest stars, was confined to a wheelchair.

It was Louis B. Mayer who rescued Lionel's sanity and bank account by planning the Dr. Kildare series, enabling Lionel to play the lovable, gruff old doctor from his chair. Lionel came to regard his wheelchair as the "best scene-stealing vehicle since the chariot in *Ben Hur*."

Lionel continued to steal scenes in forty more pictures. He also enjoyed his painting and music and was even attempting to write a novel that would sum up his own thoughtful meanderings in the field of philosophy. He never finished the manuscript. On November 15, 1954, while he was sitting on his sunny terrace reading a passage from *Macbeth,* a heart attack suddenly took his life.

Ethel's antidote for sorrow had always been her work. Now she accepted more picture roles than ever before. She was the last of the Barrymores and the last of the Drews to be performing: it was a thought to put out of her mind. Some would have turned their minds to the past, but Ethel's spirit was still youthful, although her body suffered the aching torments of old age.

She was almost lured back to the stage for a Broadway production of *The Madwoman of Chaillot,* but after some thought she finally sent the pleading producer this message: "Don't you think that after working for fifty years for cut flowers in my dressing room, I should be permitted to sit in my garden and watch them grow?"

Movie making let her do just that. She settled down first in a house and garden in Palos Verdes and later in Pacific Palisades, nearer to Hollywood. She called the Pacific Palisades house her castle. Her friends came there to pay her royal homage, and her children and grandchildren were frequently at her side.

On Ethel Barrymore's seventieth birthday, Hollywood paid her the greatest tribute ever given an actress, a nationwide radio show sponsored by the Motion Picture Academy. Voices from her past and greetings from her friends, young and old, had been recorded for the occasion. More than fifty participants paid her tribute, among them Spencer Tracy, Cary Grant, Mrs. Eleanor Roosevelt, and President Truman. All praised her talent, beauty, wit, and dedication to craftsmanship, some in flowery words, others with a tarter flavor.

One of her most devoted admirers, Katharine Hepburn, said on the program, "She has more friends than anyone I know, but she's not a dear, gentle soul. Barrymores don't come like that. She has a trenchant wit. She makes appallingly accurate observations. She doesn't know the meaning of fear or the meaning of caution . . ."

Ethel was deeply moved.

EPILOGUE

During the 1950s, Ethel was seen less frequently on the screen, and during the last eighteen months of her life, she was confined to bed as a result of arthritic rheumatism and a heart condition. She loved to listen to baseball games on the radio. She knew the batting averages of nearly all the major-league players and followed the games from opening day to the World Series. She had always been an avid reader. Now her room was crowded with books as well as flowers. She had surely not been forgotten by her friends. She had many callers.

George Cukor of the movie industry came one day. At the door he said, "May I see the most beautiful woman in California?"

Ethel's reply was, "And why have I been demoted?"

Katharine Hepburn came often. "How lucky I am to know her," she said.

On the evening of June 17, 1959, Ethel woke from a short nap, grasped her nurse's hand, and asked, "Is everybody happy? I want everybody to be happy. I know I'm happy." She fell asleep and did not wake.

The following night at the Ethel Barrymore Theater in New York City, the lights on the marquee were dimmed for five minutes before curtain time, but the play went on. Ethel would have been proud of that.

Four days later, her casket was placed in Calvary Cemetery beside those of John and Lionel. One could almost hear her say, "That's all there is. There isn't any more."

B   Fox, Mary 720102
BAR   Virginia

             Ethel Barrymore:
             a portrait

DATE			